T R I C K S
AND
SEX TOY TRICKS

More than 250 Ways to Make Good Sex Better
A Special 2-in-1 Edition

T R I C K S
AND
S E X   T O Y   T R I C K S

More than 250 Ways to Make Good Sex Better
A Special 2-in-1 Edition

Jay Wiseman

greenery press

Published in the United States by Greenery Press, 1447 Park Ave., Emeryville, CA 94608

ISBN: 0-7394-1903-X

Printed in U. S. A.

Contents

TRICKS 1

SEX TOY TRICKS 123

T R I C K S

More than 125 Ways to Make Good Sex Better

TRICKS

Table of Contents

Warning & Disclaimer 1
Sex and Creative Thinking 3
Acknowledgements 4
Why Am I Writing This Book? 5
Assumptions 7
The Limits Of Tricks 10
Intoxicants 12
A Few Don'ts Regarding Tricks 13
Fade In 15
TRICKS **19**
Menthol Tricks 85
Madonna/Whore Complex 88
Sex, Risk, Probability, and Political Correctness 89
Lubricants – Advantages, Disadvantages, and Dangers 93
Nightstand Supplies 96
What To Do If a Condom Fails 98
A Warning About SM 100
An Even Stronger Warning About Breath Control Play 103
Problems 106
Alternative Sexuality Resources 112
Bibliography 118
Please Send Me Your Tricks 120

Warning & Disclaimer

One of the riskiest things a person can do is have sex. If done in the right way, at the right time, with the right person, in the right place, and for the right reasons, sex can be one of the most wonderful experiences possible – a foretaste of heaven.

If any of the above is not right, the results can range from unpleasant to disastrous. Improper sexual acts can result in (among many other things) unplanned pregnancy, getting a fatal sexually transmitted disease, sterility, destruction of a relationship, imprisonment, suicide, and murder.

Erotic energy is one of the most powerful forces in our world. Respect and pay attention to that power and you can experience bliss. Disrespect or ignore that power and you might not live to regret it.

This book's primary purpose is to provide information and advice that will help make good sex between informed, consenting adults a little bit better. It also provides basic information to help people understand their situation, cope with problems, and find helpful resources.

Please do not think of this book as any kind of medical, legal, psychological, or other professional advice. It most certainly is not intended as a substitute for proper sex therapy. Most of its core information (particularly the "Tricks" themselves) were discovered on my own, taught to me by lovers I have had, or shared with me by friends during highly informal conversations. Please keep that in mind when considering this book's contents.

Almost without question, there are at least a few factual errors in this book, and probably a few typographical errors as well. If you have even the slightest question about the accuracy or safety of anything in here, please check with independent sources – and let me know. (By the way, please remember that not all professional advice is equally complete, accurate, up to date, and unbiased. By all means get a "second opinion" if you feel even the slightest need for one.)

No one associated with writing, editing, printing, distributing, or selling this book, or otherwise associated with it, is in any way liable for any damages that result from acting on the information herein. While I have most certainly not put anything in here that I believe would cause harm, understand clearly that you act on the information in this book entirely at your own risk.

Sex and Creative Thinking

Edward Debono, the author of various books on problem-solving and creativity, pointed out that one of the best ways to improve a situation was to look at some aspect of the situation that was already working well and figuring how to make it work even better. (Thus disproving the tired, self-defeating cliche of "if it's not broken, don't fix it.")

He pointed out that, while solving problems was clearly important, you could often make even greater gains by improving something that was already working well. For example, a store in financial trouble can often do better by increasing its income than by cutting expenses.

This book was written in accordance with the "improve what's already working well" principle. It assumes that your sex life and your relationship are already in good shape and goes from there. (It also, however, includes basic referrals if the above assumptions are not true.)

Acknowledgements
(The "Thank You" List)

While I promised not to attribute a particular Trick to a particular person (also, it wasn't rare for a Trick to be suggested by more than one individual), all the folks listed below contributed at least one Trick, or other useful information, to this book.

Ann Grogan
Annagreta Carver
Augusta Fury
Anonymous
Bill Burns
Bob Shurtleff
Brenda Love
Charles Moser
Don Melius
Donna Fitzgerald
Don't You Dare Use My Name
Hank Stephenson
Informed Sources
Institute for Advanced Study of
    Human Sexuality, San Francisco
Jana
Janet Hardy
KAT

Kathleen Wood
Keep My Name Out Of It
Lorilee Rainey
Lynn Craig
Mara Soulara
Maria Isaacs
Mariposa
Mic Bergen
Mystie Grey
Only If You Swear Not To Use My
    Name
Quickchick
Sage
San Francisco Sex Information
Stephanie Wadell
Ted McIlvenna
Walter Shelbourne

Why Am I Writing This Book?

Because the World Can Use A Little More Pleasure

Part of me wonders why I continue writing books about sex. It's an interest of mine, but not my primary interest or my only interest. I'm planning, gathering material for, or working on books about the martial arts, humor, ambulance work, writing, creative thinking, and other areas. Also, I confess that I find writing about sex, and therefore being identified as a "significantly sexual" person, ever so slightly embarrassing.

I decided to write this particular book for a number of reasons. It was fun to write and, as my friends have gleefully pointed out, fun to research. Writing it didn't take long – much less time than other books I'm either working on or planning. It will help many people with an important, often difficult part of their lives. (The amount of "sexual illiteracy" in our society astounds me.) Candidly, the fact that this book will probably sell well has not escaped me.

But there is a more important reason. I believe that pleasure is, in and of itself, a good, positive, and desirable thing. That is a relatively rare view in our society. Many, many people distrust pleasure engaged in for its own sake. The feeling is that there is something corrupting about pleasure. Many people believe that experiencing pleasure can readily lead to physical, emotional, social, and other forms of decay. People who seek pleasure, particularly *sexual* pleasure, risk being regarded as lazy, slothful, irresponsible, wasteful, sinful, and so forth.

In my experience, that is simply not true. It is certainly true that pleasure (in any form) can be pursued to the neglect of one's responsibilities. No doubt about that. But my feeling is that cart-before-thehorse reasoning often occurs regarding this issue. People who pursue pleasure so intensely that they neglect their responsibilities reveal a defect in themselves. The pleasure did not cause this defect. It was already there. Please don't blame the wrong party.

Pleasure eases stress and calms nervous minds. Sharing pleasure leads to increased intimacy and stronger relationships. Experiencing pleasure reduces hatred, calms violent feelings, and helps relieve sadness, grief, and depression. In short, pleasure contributes good both to individuals and to humankind as a whole in many different ways.

People accept that humor does that. Why do they have so much trouble accepting it of pleasure? Our puritanical heritage, I guess.

Seeking after pleasure, including sexual pleasure, can – like absolutely everything else – can be done to unwarranted and detrimental extremes, but let us understand that pleasure itself is a good and positive thing, possibly even a divine gift.

Assumptions

In presenting the information in this book, I am making the following assumptions about your situation. If these assumptions are not true in your case, please adjust your behavior accordingly.

I'm assuming:

1. That both of you are willing (and, hopefully, eager) to have sex with each other. Consent is absolutely essential.

2. That having sex with each other will not violate any agreements you made with other people about your sexual conduct.

3. That both of you understand the nature of what you are doing. Having sex with someone too young, feeble-minded, senile, intoxicated, or otherwise unable to understand and consent to what is happening may get you charged with rape, even if no force was used. Remember, if they're too drunk to drive, they're probably too drunk to have sex.

4. That both of you have reached the age of consent your state (and that you live in the United States). I believe the age of consent is as low as 12 in at least one state and as high as 18 in many others. Remember, an act that is perfectly legal on one side of a state line might get you a lengthy prison sentence on the other side. Make certain you know the age of consent in your state.

    Your local library should have a copy of your state's criminal code in its reference section. Reading its sections on rape, incest, indecent exposure, lewd and lascivious conduct, assault, contributing to the delinquency of a minor, and related sections may be very informative. Asking a local attorney or police officer can also help, but remember that opinions, knowledge, and objectivity can vary widely, even among such "experts." Try to talk to more than one source.

(By the way, sex between blood relatives may be illegal no matter what the age of those involved. If you cannot legally marry a particular person, it may also be illegal for you to have sex with them. This could be true even if both of you are over 21 and both fully consent.)

5.   That the acts I'm describing are legal in your state. Although the laws are rarely enforced, oral sex, anal intercourse and other practices are still a crime in some states, even if done by consenting adults in private. Find out your state's laws (and, where appropriate, work to change them).

6.   That there is no risk of passing on a sexually transmitted disease. If such a risk does exist, please modify what you do. Among other things, if you have herpes or have tested positive for the AIDS virus and have sex with someone without first telling them about that, you could be arrested. You could also get sued if your partner becomes infected.

If you have any questions, one resource is the National Sexually Transmitted Disease Hotline at (800) 227-8922.

Criteria

For inclusion in this book, a Trick usually had to meet the following criteria:

1.   It had to be something that could be done pretty much on impulse in the here and now. Nothing too elaborate.

2.   It had to involve minimal equipment, preferably nothing outside the bodies of the people involved. If it did involve equipment, it usually had to be something found in the average household.

3.   It had to be safe. I included nothing I thought likely to endanger people.

4.   It had to pertain directly to sex or to a very closely related matter.

5.   It had to have a successful track record. I looked for Tricks that had consistently made more than one lover gasp, sigh, and moan.

6.   It had to appeal to a wide, mainstream audience. The Trick couldn't be too far out or kinky. (Some of my other books do include kinkier material – there is a "Spanking Tricks" section in "Tricks 2," and a great deal of detail regarding erotic power games in "SM 101.") Most of the Tricks therefore involve masturbation, fellatio, cunnilingus, vaginal intercourse, and anal intercourse.

Selection and Balance

The Tricks in this book reflect the material I received. For example, there are more fellatio Tricks listed than cunnilingus Tricks. This reflects the comments and suggestions I received, not any deliberate editing or selectivity on my part. (Indeed, I actively sought as many cunnilingus Tricks as I could.) This may also reflect the fact that, as a group, the women I interviewed were considerably more forthcoming than the men I interviewed.

I've tried to present as many Tricks as possible in a "gender neutral" manner. In most cases, it doesn't matter whether the people involved are straight, bisexual or gay.

Please remember that I plan to publish more additions to the series of "Tricks" books. If you feel a certain category is underrepresented, by all means send in material to balance things out.

I deliberately included many masturbation Tricks in this book as my own way of encouraging safer sex.

I decided to, for the most part, leave out material regarding SM, bisexuality, swinging, tantra, multiple-partner sex, and so forth. Those are specialized areas, and their practices and customs are far too extensive to describe properly in this book. I included contact information if you're interested in exploring them further.

The Limits Of Tricks

You know, and I know, that lovemaking cannot be reduced to Tricks. Tricks are to erotic play what spices are to eating. A few carefully chosen ones make the experience more intense and pleasurable. Too many spoil things. Remember, this book is about how to give things that are already going well a boost.

It's entirely possible to have a wonderful and completely satisfying sex life without knowing any of the Tricks in this book, or any others. Good sex is based on caring about your partner's well being, really wanting to have sex with them (and, of course them really wanting to have sex with you), and observing the responsibilities that go with that. Still, adding a carefully chosen spice now and then can enhance the experience.

Key Point: Your underlying feelings towards the other person, and theirs toward you, greatly affect whether or not a Trick will improve your erotic play. As one lady told me, "If I really like him, then he almost can't do anything wrong. If I really don't like him, then he can't even breathe right."

When a Trick Bombs

Each person has their own unique physical and emotional pattern of erotic responsiveness. Among other things, that means every now and then a Trick that has always worked well before may utterly turn off a new partner. The key phrase for handling this situation is "show compassion for everyone, including yourself."

If what you did really turned your partner off, perhaps even disgusted them, try not to take it too personally. (You wouldn't be human if you didn't take it somewhat personally, but try not to buy into that too deeply.) Remember, each person has their own pattern, and you can never completely know what that pattern looks like. Give them a brief apology, if that seems appropriate, then do what you can to move on to something else. There is little to be gained by stopping to argue or debate the point in depth, particularly right then. Save discussions for later.

On the other hand, if your partner starts to do something that really doesn't work for you, please diplomatically let them know that as soon as you can. "Being polite" in this situation will only allow your displeasure to build to uncontrollable levels. Speak up (politely, please) as soon as possible. Remember, this is almost undoubtedly not willful misconduct on their part. They are probably doing it in an attempt, however misguided, to arouse you. Speak up, but give them the benefit of the doubt, especially if this partner is relatively new.

Find Their Envelope

Tricks don't work well in isolation. Each person has their own erotic response pattern, something I've come to think of as their "envelope." One of your main tasks as a good lover is to find your partner's envelope. Something that is wildly erotic for one person can be grossly unpleasant, even traumatic, for another.

The envelope varies widely from person to person. It also varies over time with the same person. An experience once thought repulsive can become highly attractive, and vice versa. Find their envelope before you try too many Tricks, and remember that the location and content of that envelope change over time.

Intoxicants

Provided you don't have a substance abuse problem, light use of intoxicants can do a lot to enhance your mood. They can relax tense muscles, take your mind off the worries of the day, and generally calm you down and bring you into the here and now.

I prefer wine. Beer tends to fill up my bladder too quickly (and too often). Harder liquors take me more out of it than I like. I quit using recreational drugs of any kind many years ago.

More than light intoxicant use is asking for trouble. Your judgment becomes dangerously cloudy. Your coordination suffers. You may become too out of it to be sexual at all.

AIDS prevention experts are campaigning against combining sex and intoxicants. They have found that many unsafe sex acts occur when and – more importantly – only when the people involved are intoxicated. They compare driving under the influence (D.U.I.) with having sex under the influence (S.U.I.) in terms of danger.

Remember that getting someone too drunk or stoned to understand what is happening and then having sex with them is rape.

As a rule, if you get someone too drunk or stoned that it would be a crime for them to drive, then it would also probably be a crime to have sex with them.

A Few Don'ts Regarding Tricks (and Other Matters)

1. Don't spend too much time doing Tricks. It's far more important to stay in the here and now with your lover. Do a Trick "every now and then."

2. Don't try to do too many different Tricks in a single session. Again, doing that distances you from your lover.

3. Don't be overly concerned with looking for opportunities to do a Trick. Let such opportunities appear naturally during the course of events. Men seem particularly vulnerable to this pitfall– thus giving rise to the somewhat bitter saying among many women, "There were three of us in bed. Me, him, and his technique."

4. Never place anything in a woman's vagina if it's recently been in her (or, for that matter, any other person's) anus. Doing so can cause her to get an infection that will require a visit to a doctor and antibiotics to cure. For example, inserting your penis or a dildo into her anus and then into her vagina would be very likely cause such an infection. (A physician once told me that licking a woman's anus and then licking her vagina could cause her to get infected.) Anything used for anal play must first be thoroughly cleaned before it can be used for vaginal play.

5. Never seal your mouth over a woman's vagina and blow air into it. There are reports of women suffering fatal air embolisms

from this practice. Menstruating and pregnant women seem to face a considerably higher than average risk. Such incidents are very, very rare, but they do happen.

6.   Be careful about placing food items in a woman's vagina, especially sugary foods. Many men and women recommended placing various foods in there and then eating them out. (Grapes had something of a cult following.) These foods can upset the natural balance and cause infections, particularly yeast infections. You can do such Tricks if you want, but if you do, then understand that you may have to deal with their effects "the morning after."

Fade In

Imagine that you are at an informal dinner party for eight to ten highly open-minded people. You know five of the other people there, but not the other four. None of you is a health-care professional.

The food (quite delicious, by the way) has been served and the guests are now lingering over the remnants of their desserts, coffee, and after-dinner drinks. The conversation, somehow or other, turns to sex play. One of the husbands describes something he does in bed that drives his wife (who is sitting next to him) crazy in bed. She blushes a bit, but is not really angry. Instead, she pipes up with, "Oh, yeah? Well let me tell you what turns *him* on." She then proceeds to do exactly that, and it's now his turn to blush a little.

This exchange, as such exchanges often do, prompts another guest to share one of their favorite bedroom pleasures, and now the whole table joins in with enthusiasm.

Dozens of comments follow, incorporating such phrases as "I just love it when someone..." and "I know I can always drive a guy wild when I..." Other comments include, "I just hate it when someone..." and "One thing I learned the hard way was..." And so it continues, for well over an hour. People pour out their special caresses, Tricks they do with their mouths, ways to keep out of trouble, and special techniques for adding extra heat to an already hot situation.

When the conversation finally lapses, there's a moment of slightly embarrassed silence, and the dinner party begins to break up. A few of the couples, their eyes slightly smoldering, seem in a politely eager hurry to return to their homes. One of the men makes a few discreet notes on a napkin. At this point, the scene fades out.

I want you to regard the Tricks and other information in this book much as you would regard what you would hear at such a dinner party. None of it is any sort of professional or expert advice, but most of it seems to make sense – and of course you will independently check on matters you have questions about before trying them yourself.

Fade In
/////////////////////////////////

• • • •
1
• • • •

Hooker's Trick #1

Most men like to watch. Therefore, when asked
to give head, many hookers position themselves
so their customer can see his cock entering their mouth. ⌘
Footnote: If you feel like teasing him, position yourself so he
cannot see his cock entering your mouth.

• • • •
2
• • • •

Rubbing At The Gate

Just before the man enters the woman, when she is fully
aroused and ready to receive him, he takes his penis in one
hand and rubs its tip gently and sensuously against her
genitals, especially on her clitoris and between her vaginal
lips. This can also be done during intercourse
- the penis is removed, rubbed for a while,
then reinserted.

⋮3⋮

Milking It For All It's Worth

When a man comes, the sensations of orgasm mix with the
sensations of semen passing through his penis. Interestingly
enough, his orgasm usually doesn't pump
all the semen out of his penis; some remains behind. During
masturbation or fellatio, a considerate lover can give him a
tiny "extra" orgasm by pinching his cock lightly but firmly and
"milking" this remaining fluid from his penis after his
"regular" orgasm has finished. ⌘ You can even put your
thumb on the base of his penis and your finger at the rear top
of his scrotum and milk that section forward, then bring your
hand forward and milk the penis from base to tip, producing a
more complete emptying. (Be sure you don't painfully squeeze
his testicles.) Your lover can try this when he masturbates to
find what method feels best, then teach it to you. ⌘ This
can also be done by him, and perhaps by you, during vaginal or
anal intercourse. Withdraw the penis most (not all) of the
way, milk it, then reinsert. Ah, bliss.

:4:

Blowing Hot And Cold

This Trick is fairly simple, but effective. If you gently blow on something (such as a nipple, penis, or vagina) from very close, your breath feels hot. If you back off about six to twelve inches and blow, your breath feels cold. Wetting the blown-upon object with your saliva increases both sensations. Hot and cold can be alternated to good effect. This can be combined well with masturbation and "regular" oral sex.

:5:

A Condom Ain't Enough

It's possible for a condom to break or slip off without either party noticing. (Both have happened to me.)
Therefore, if you're in a situation where you need to use a condom, then by definition you are in a situation where you need to use *more* than a condom. A spermicidal jelly or foam, or a lubricant containing *very* generous quantities of nonoxynol-9 (at least 2%), would be a good choice. Although current medical thought is that nonoxynol-9 does not protect against HIV transmission, it's still a good spermicide and will help at least somewhat in preventing pregnancy.

....6....
Starting At The Bottom

Have your lover lie on their stomach. Place the broad, flat part of your tongue at the bottom of the small of their back and run your tongue quickly up their spine, all the way to the top of their neck. The guy who told me of this said, "If this doesn't get a gasp out of her, she's dead."

....7....
Brush Strokes

It's entirely true that most women like to have their genitals caressed. However, another spot close by feels almost as good. Have her spread her legs (this works well if she's on her back) and, using your fingertips, lightly stroke the upper insides of her thighs, particularly the rear portions.

This stroking can be done in a back and forth or circular motion, or you can slowly trace your way toward her vagina.

You can also use your tongue effectively this way.

(Rumor has it that many men also find the touch of efingertips or a tongue here pleasant.)

·:8·:
Pin The Skin

Grasp the erect penis with your thumb and forefinger
just below its tip. (If you are right-handed, this would
probably work best if you used your left hand.) Keep your
grasp slightly firm, and slide your hand down the shaft
of the penis to its base. You should now have his penis in your
hand with its skin pulled somewhat tight over it.
You may see its head slightly but noticeably bulge when you
pull the skin down.   ⌘   Normally, when a man masturbates,
gets his cock sucked, or has intercourse, this skin slides.
Pinning the skin in place and then stimulating his penis
produces a noticeably more intense, usually highly
pleasurable, sensation. One caution:
Stimulation may feel rough and unpleasant if the penis is dry,
so use enough lubricant to keep things slippery, especially
during masturbation.

·:9·:
The Nays Have It

When performing cunnilingus, position
your lips or tongue over her clitoris, then
rapidly shake your head from side to side.
This can be done in a series of short shakes,
or in a long one. Just don't do it for too long or it can
make you dizzy, and getting really carried away might injure
your neck.

:10:

Don't Race For The Top

Many a woman reports that it feels better
when you lick and caress the sides of her clitoris
rather than its top.

:11:

A Warm, Wet Touch

Our genitals remain very sensitive after we've had sex. One
thing that can feel great is to get a washrag moistened with
warm water and place it there. I once had a lover that, as I
was lying there feeling somewhat exhausted, would get up,
prepare the washrag, and place it on me. Oh, bliss! To this
day, I have fond memories of her. ⌘ Safety note: Make sure
the water is comfortably warm, but not too hot! Test it on
your elbow before placing it on them.

12
Before and After

During his orgasm, and for about a minute afterward,
the head of a man's penis is likely to be much more sensitive
to touch that it is at other times. Therefore, any touching
there is felt much more intensely than it is felt at
other times - so much so that touching it may be painful. ⌘
Some men like to have the head of their cock rubbed briskly
when they come, some like to have it left alone, and some like
to have it lightly stroked. Your partner can tell you which he
likes. Just remember that strokes which felt wonderful
to him before he reached orgasm may feel agonizing during
and immediately afterwards.

:13:

Tap Dancing

For this Trick, the woman lies on her back with her legs comfortably spread and you lie on your side beside her, perhaps propped up on one elbow. Place the palm of your hand on her mons (the mound where most of her pubic hair is), and rest your fingers lightly on her vaginal lips. ⌘ Lightly but firmly press your palm onto her mons and begin to move your hand in a tiny circular motion. Your palm should not slide too much over her skin during this process. Instead, her skin should move underneath it. Repeat this process until you have done ten circles. ⌘ You then raise your fingers and lightly tap her vaginal lips about once a second until you have given her ten taps. Please note that these are light taps, not spanks. They shouldn't hurt. ⌘ After giving the taps, rest your hand for five to ten seconds. Then repeat the circles, then repeat the taps, then rest again, then repeat the circles... ⌘ The woman who eagerly told me about this technique swore that it drove her "absolutely bonkers."

14

Safewords

Safewords are special words lovers use to indicate that "the game" needs to be slowed down or stopped. Safewords first became widespread in SM circles. ⌘ To prevent possibly disastrous misunderstandings, lovers need special signals to indicate that one of them "really" needs to have what's going on slowed down or stopped. Safewords fill that need. ⌘ Safewords are usually chosen from words not likely to otherwise come up. "Yellow" is often used to signal "let's ease up or slow down." "Red" is often used to signal, "Stop what's going on. I *really* mean it." ⌘ Failure to honor a safeword is an extremely serious offense – in some cases even a crime. *Never* joke or kid around with safewords.

.15.

Climbing The Mountain

This masturbation game can drive a man absolutely nuts. It's usually done with him lying on his back. Sit or kneel either beside him or between his legs. Take his penis in one hand and gently, sensuously caress it for about ten seconds, then give it one quick up-and-down stroke. Repeat the sensuous caressing for about ten seconds - perhaps doing slow up-and-down strokes, perhaps doing other things that feel good - and then give his penis two quick up-and-down strokes. Repeat the sensual caressing, then give three quick strokes. Then more caressing, followed by four quick strokes. Then more caressing, and five strokes. You get the idea. ⌘ Continue to "climb the mountain" as long as you can. One tip: The man may reach a point where his orgasm is becoming inevitable, and slow caressing might spoil it. He is therefore allowed to say (assuming he can still coherently speak) "keep going" one time, after which you give him only rapid strokes until he comes. He should climax within about one minute.

:16:
Push Here To Start

After she is aroused, sit between her legs. Gently insert one
finger deeply into her vagina and, when she's ready, insert a
second. Then take your thumb and place it against her anus.
Don't insert it. Instead, gently press there while you move
your fingers. My highly reliable source tells me that, while
many women are turned off by the idea of having something
inserted into their anus, they often like feeling this kind of
pressure there. (Note: See Point #4 under "A Few Don'ts
Regarding Tricks.")

:17:
Flat Top

Hold the shaft of his penis in one hand so that it points straight
away from his body. Stiffen the palm and fingers of your other
(well lubricated) hand and place your palm on the head of his
penis. Lightly but firmly rub your palm to and
fro, side to side, in clockwise circles, and
in counter-clockwise circles. You can
also tilt your hand front and rear or side
to side. This technique involves a lot of
stimulation directly on one of the most
sensitive parts of a man's body, so make
sure it doesn't get so intense that it becomes
unpleasant. Watching his face will give you clues.

18

Give Her What She Wants
(Most Of The Time)

During cunnilingus or masturbation, when you find something that really turns her on, don't do it continuously. Do it for "a while," then do something else pleasurable for ten to fifteen seconds, then go back to doing what she likes.

19

Hooker's Trick #2

To help make the guy come, use your fingertips to lightly tap the underside of his scrotum.

20

Backing Up

The initial entry of anal intercourse is often the most painful part for the receptive partner. This can often be dealt with by holding the penis or dildo stationary and letting them "back" onto it at their own pace. ⌘ Footnote: Entry can also be made easier if the receptive person "bears down" (like they do when having a bowel movement) as the object is inserted.

•:•
.21.
•••

Orgasm Vs. Ejaculation

For many men, they only overlap to a certain degree.
(I've heard it may be possible to separate them entirely.)
In my case, for example, I have noticed that I sometimes
ejaculate quite a bit at the very beginning of my orgasm,
long before the feelings reach their peak. (Therefore I
probably shouldn't try to use the withdrawal method
of birth control, or promise not to come in my lover's mouth.)
⌘ Furthermore, my orgasm lasts for nearly a minute,
continuing after I have stopped ejaculating.
I once got slightly irked with a lover when she stopped
masturbating me because "all the sperm had stopped coming
out." I explained to her, and we never had that problem
again. ⌘ Remember, they're two different things.

•••
.22.
•••

Vampire Attack #1

Have your lover lie on their stomach,
then lightly bite your way up and
down their spine.

23

A Bit of The Bubbly

When performing fellatio, stopping occasionally
to place a sip of champagne in your mouth and
then reinserting his penis can liven things up
wonderfully. (A soft drink can provide a nice
non-alcoholic alternative.)

24

Ice Cube Trick #1

When performing fellatio, holding a small ice
cube in your mouth helps focus his attention.
(This Trick is slightly risky. See "Menthol Tricks" for
more information.)

25

"Show Me How You Like It"

Let's say you are masturbating your partner and things just
aren't getting anywhere. Instead of continuing until both of
you are exhausted and sore, get some coaching. Ask your
partner to "show me how you like it" and observe their
stroking pattern. The woman who taught me this Trick was a
bisexual sex worker who has had many, many partners of both
sexes. She went on to remark, "Men are more standard;
women are more individualistic."

:26:
Pennies From Heaven

For this Trick, your lover lies on their back with their hands at
their sides and their palms facing down.

Place a coin on top of each ankle and on the back of each
hand. The game is simple. You try to turn them on so much
that they move and the coins fall off. They, on the other hand,
try to hold still.

:27:
Sponging Off

Ladies, if you want to have sex during your period without
getting blood all over the place, go to the cosmetics
department and buy a small natural sea sponge called a
cosmetic sponge.   ⌘   Shortly before sex, soak the sponge in
water to soften it, then squeeze the water out and insert the
sponge into your vagina so that it's close to your cervix.
There's a good chance your lover will never
notice any blood or detect the sponge.   ⌘
Afterwards, remove it (fishing it out with
your fingers may be a bit of a nuisance),
rinse it with cold water, wash it with
soap and hot water, and perhaps rinse it
with hydrogen peroxide.

28

Hot Dog In A Bun

The man snuggles up closely behind the woman while they
both lie on their sides, like two spoons. He inserts his penis
between (not into) her labia so that the head of his penis rests
against her clitoris. She then lightly squeezes her legs together
and they begin intercourse-like thrusting motions. The woman
who told me about this Trick mentioned that it could make
having regular intercourse rather "anti-climactic."

29

First Come, First Served

A masturbation race! Whoever reaches orgasm first wins,
and gets a dinner – or some other prize. Fun alternatives can
involve masturbating, or performing oral sex on, each other.
As to whether or not any woman involved has come (the age-
old question), you just have to trust her.

30

Thumb Enchanted Evening

Kneel behind your lover while she is on her hands and knees
facing away from you (dog-style position). Use your thumb to
pleasure the inside of her vagina while the side of your index
finger caresses her clitoris.

·31·

Double Blind Studies

In this Trick, *both* of you are blindfolded while you explore
and pleasure each other's bodies. No cheating! A room that
can be fully darkened offers another alternative. Note: Your
local drugstore or variety store may carry excellent,
inexpensive blindfolds known as sleep masks.

·32·

Let's Neck

The back of a lover's neck is a more sensitive and erotic place
than most people think. Caresses, kisses, licks, and light bites
here often produce a powerful effect.

·33·

Dress for the Occasion

One excellent way for a man to learn to
associate erotic sensations with a condom
is to masturbate while wearing one.

:34:
Vampire Attack #2

Your lover arches their head back and you lightly
bite them on the neck. Bite to the side of their windpipe,
where the major veins and arteries lie, and hold the
bite for a long count. Your may feel the throbbing of the main
artery in their neck. Then release the bite and allow them to
do the same to you. The man who told me about this
Trick said that it was a trust thing that tapped into deep,
primal feelings – and was known for the powerful effect it
could have on those who did it.

:35:
I Want a Caveman

Gently but firmly grip their hair in a way that puts their
head under your control. Slide your hand up their back
and neck, with your fingers pointing upwards and slightly
spread, until your hand slides "under" their hair and your palm
rests on the lower rear of their head. Then grip their hair.
(Don't grip so hard that you hurt them.) This
is a powerful technique and many people don't like it, but
those who enjoy "surrendering" to their lover
may find it wonderfully overwhelming.

·36·
Speaking In Tongues

Have you ever placed your tongue on a nipple, penis, or clitoris and not really known what to do with it? If routine licking starts to seem boring after a while, become a person of letters. Use your tongue to trace out letters. Spell your name. Spell their name. "Write" the alphabet. Use all capital letters. Use all lower case letters. Use both printing and cursive writing. Of course, there's also numbers, and punctuation marks, and other symbols, and the Greek alphabet, and...

·37·
Hooker's Trick #3

Many (if not most) men, while they're being fellated, like to come in their partner's mouth. Unfortunately, not everyone loves the taste of semen. My sources tell me that you won't taste it as much if you place your tongue over the head of his penis shortly before he comes, and I can tell you firsthand that it's difficult to detect any difference in sensation when this is done to you.

∴38∴
Common Sense Ideas

Lovemaking involves all the senses. Therefore, when planning
a get-together, contemplate each sense in turn. Other than
each other, consider what you would like to see, what you
would like to hear, and what would you like to smell, touch,
and taste.

∴39∴
Up, Down, Up, and Off

When setting up your bedroom to create "your own little
world," it can help to run down the following checklist. ⌘
Turn *up* the heat. Most people need a temperature of at least
75 degrees to feel comfortable while naked. ⌘ Turn *down*
the lights. Candles and low wattage bulbs are nice. Dimmer
switches on regular lights can be useful. Drapes and blinds can
be adjusted. Softer lights make the situation more intimate.

Also, most of us look better under soft lighting than we
lookunder a blinding spotlight. ⌘ Turn *up* the music. Again,
this adds atmosphere. It also helps keep "unique" sounds
private. ⌘ Turn *off* the phone's ringer. There is something
about a ringing phone that is almost irresistible. Let your voice
mail or answering machine take the call (and turn down the
answering machine's volume).

·:40:·

Rub Them the Right Way

While erotic tension can add to sex, stress-related tension doesn't help. One excellent way to help your partner relax before things "get serious" is to give them a facial massage. ⌘ Have your partner lie comfortably on their back and sit or kneel at their head, facing their toes. Mentally draw a line down the middle of their face. ⌘ Start at the top. Place your fingertips at the middle of their forehead and gently but firmly spread them apart. At the end of the stroke, lift your fingers off of your lover's skin and bring them back together at the center of their forehead, slightly below where your first stroke started. Repeat this stroke pattern down their face. Ask your partner to tell you if they would like the strokes to be heavier, lighter, or otherwise changed. Pay extra attention to the areas above the eyes, below the eyes (don't press on the eyes themselves), under the nose, and both lips.

•41•

Fast and Easy

Among the many lessons I learned during my days as an ambulance crewman were two that apply to sex. 1. If you don't keep it handy, you won't use it. 2. If it's not easy to use, you won't use it. ⌘ During the terrible rush of dealing with a life-threatening emergency, special equipment was often overlooked (often to the patient's detriment) because using it "would have taken too much time" or "was too much trouble." Objectively, neither of those statements was usually true, but during an emergency, they certainly *felt* as though they were true. ⌘ The same applies to a sexual encounter. If you have to rummage in a drawer for lubricant, fumble around in the dark for a vibrator, and so forth, a "just forget it" feeling emerges. A good general rule is that anything that takes longer than *five seconds* to get or to set up will not be used. ⌘ Remember the critical importance of these concepts when considering where and how to store your safer sex and birth control supplies.

:42:

Make a Tent

If you're in bed and looking for a simple but
effective way to spice up masturbating a penis,
simply drape the sheet over it while you stroke.
Just remember that you may need a clean sheet
in the very near future.

:43:

A Hair-Raising Trick

Grasp your lover's pubic hair in such a way that the middle
joints of your fingers and the heel of your palm rest on their
pubic mound. Then move your hand up and down, from side to
side, and in circles. You can also tilt your hand in various
directions. The intensity of this movement can be increased
until you are actually rocking your partner. ⌘ Caution: This
"rough foreplay" Trick may involve mild to moderate amounts
of pain. It probably won't work on most
people. I recommend you try it only on
someone who is already highly aroused.
Watch their face and body very carefully
to see how they react. Continue only if
there's no doubt that they are enjoying it.

Fill 'er Up

Many women report that their orgasms feel more intense and satisfying if there's something in their vagina when they come. Keep this in mind when masturbating a woman or performing cunnilingus.

45

Speak Up #1

Good sex is closely related to your ability to stay "here and now and involved in what's happening." Anything that interferes with that detracts from the experience. Correct anything that bothers you early, and as diplomatically as possible. Are you cold? Is the music too loud? Is your position uncomfortable? Correct those things before they grow from minor annoyances into serious disruptions.

:46:
Speak Up #2

People can feel nervous during sex, especially during their first time with a new lover. Talking may relax and de-inhibit both parties. (This need not necessarily be "dirty" or "erotic" talk, although those arouse many people.) Talking to your partner can help them reach orgasm. The proper kind and amount of talk will vary from lover to lover – feedback is important. Still, as the retired courtesan who told me about this remarked, "We really miss out by having silence in the bedroom."

:47:
Mirror Images

Being able to see yourselves can add a lot, and many bedrooms have mirrors propped up this way and that. Some are in fixed positions, others are movable. Mirrors mounted directly over the bed are a long-time favorite but, since the 1989 earthquake, many people in the San Francisco area switched from glass to unbreakable mylar mirrors.

48
Men's Chests Need Love Too

Several women reported to me that men's chests, especially their nipples, were more sensitive to stroking, light scratching, licking, sucking, and friendly biting than the men thought.

49
Feeling Good All Over

For many men, the only touching that feels erotic to them is touching on their genitals. (For some men, it's only their penis. Even touching their scrotum doesn't feel erotic.) One good way to eroticize more of a man's body is to touch and stroke (or, perhaps, lick and suck) his penis and, at the same time, touch and stroke another part of his body. His scrotum, nipples, and inner thighs are good places to start. In many cases, pleasurable sensations will be built up over time. ⌘ One tip: Don't try to eroticize too many different places at the same time. Spend a few sessions on just his nipples, for example, before working on other areas.

:50:

Bondage Safety Tip #1: Loss of Sensation

I'm not going to describe bondage techniques in this book.
That is a specialized area that requires a book of its own.
I've written such a book, and you can find out how to get a
copy in the back of this book. I will only say here that
bondage is becoming a major area of experimentation for
many, many people. (A recent article in the San Francisco
Chronicle mentioned that 25% of all adults have experimented
with it.) Because it's an area of such immense interest, I will
describe a few basic safety tips. ⌘ There is never any
need to tie any body part so tightly that it loses feeling. If
some part of your lover's body "goes to sleep," then it's time
to loosen whatever's causing that.

.51.
Bondage Safety Tip #2: Quick Release

If you tie someone up, you must have some method of releasing them quickly. That means you must be able to get them completely free within sixty seconds, and preferably within thirty seconds. ⌘ One basic safety precaution is to keep a pair of scissors handy so you can cut your lover free in an emergency such as a fire or earthquake. The large, plastic-handled "paramedic scissors" popular with rescue squads are an excellent choice because, unlike regular bandage scissors, they were designed to cut through leather, webbing, and other heavy materials quickly. These scissors are available at many medical supply stores. The more health-conscious and responsible leather stores and erotic boutiques also carry them. ⌘ Knots in nylon stockings and silk scarves – often the first choice of beginners – are notoriously difficult to untie if they've been pulled very tight. Don't use anything you're not willing to cut through if necessary.

:52:

Bondage Safety Tip #3: Stay With Them

Many people think it would be fun to "tie them up
and then go off and leave them." In fact, this is one of the
most irresponsible things you can do. You are responsible if
your partner is injured in any way while you are gone.
You may also face criminal charges. Here's a simple rule:
Stay as close to a bound person, and check on them as often,
as you would an infant left in your care. Don't leave them
alone, not even if they ask you to.

.53.

Bondage Safety Tip #4:
Emergency Lighting

A bound person must be closely watched. In an emergency, they must be freed. To do both of these, you need light. A power failure during a normal sexual encounter can be, at the least, annoying. A power failure during a bondage session can be a serious – even life-threatening – problem. ⌘ Therefore, responsible bondage fans always make sure they have emergency light sources immediately available. Flashlights, especially light-colored ones that are easy to see in dim light, are carried in pockets, stored in specific places in "toy bags," and otherwise placed where they can be easily found in the dark. ⌘ Furthermore, increasing numbers of bedrooms and "playrooms" now have "blackout lights" – lights that come on automatically if the power fails – plugged into their wall sockets. Basic models that will do nicely for the average-sized room can be bought at drugstores, variety stores, and similar places for around ten to twenty dollars.

:54:
The Ties That Don't Bind

While I'm not going to describe how to tie someone up (in this book, anyway), I will say that it can be great fun to have your partner pretend they are tied in a certain position and then "have your way" with them. Indeed, sometimes the "bound" person gets so carried away by what's being done to them that it really doesn't matter that they're not "actually" tied up.

:55:
Table the Motion

My sources tell me that you can "do" someone with your hands, mouth, and "helpful devices" very effectively if you have them lie on the dining room table, or a similar place. Please make very, very sure that the table can support their (slightly thrashing) weight. Think twice, double-check the table, and think twice again before joining them on it. Light padding, especially under their head, is often a welcome supplemental touch.

.56.
Perineum Pinch

One man reports that many different women
enjoy having him insert his index finger in their anus
and his thumb in their vagina. These are then pinched
together, thrust in and out, rocked back and forth, twisted,
and so forth. (A latex glove might make this Trick safer and
more comfortable for both people. For more information see
"A Few Don'ts Regarding Tricks" chapter.)

.57.
Nature is a Mother

Here's the big tip for sex on the beach, in the woods, and so
forth. Bring a blanket! ⌘ Various bits of "Mother Nature"
have a way of getting in the most awkward places,
at the most awkward times, unless you bring something,
preferably something *wide*, to lie on.

:58:

Beware of the Daily Grind

The pace of life is increasing, and many of us are chronically tired, stressed, and sleep-deprived. Among other things, some of them medically serious, such a pace can easily erode our relationships and drain us of the time and energy we need for high-quality lovemaking. ⌘ Scheduling time for "rest and recreation" can bring back the shine to a relationship, and to sex. This can be as simple as leaving a Sunday afternoon free or as elaborate as planning a two-week trip. Just remember, the key is to schedule as much free time as possible. ⌘ Don't spend all of your free time doing "catch up" work. Remember that the daily grind is one of the most serious hazards your relationship faces.

:59:

Cleanliness Is Next To...

Oils, lubricants, and other "messy" materials can get all over the place. Therefore, to spare your bedspread, carpet, and similar items, take down and spread out your (very clean) shower curtain with the inside surface facing up. Among other things, this arrangement allows for "easy clean up."

:60:

When Is a Whip Not a Whip?

People who experiment very lightly with flagellation games
tell me that a rolled-up pillowcase can make an interesting
"whip." It provides small amounts of noise, creates a sensation
of "thud," causes little if any pain, and almost never leaves
marks. This would not be a bad starting point for any
experimentation you felt like doing in this area. Remember to
establish safewords (see Trick #14).

:61:

A Peachy Idea

One young lady told me that a peach pit, when used
while still wet and slick, is excellent for clitoral stimulation.
(Be careful of its sharp, pointy end!) She said its
combination of smoothness, roughness, and wetness
made it feel a lot like a tongue.

⁞62⁞

Silence Isn't Golden

Many people reported that their arousal decreased if their
partner didn't seem to be responding to what was happening.
If you like what your lover is doing with their hand or mouth
(or something else) let them know. It's not necessary to put
on a big show, but let out any sighs, groans, or gasps that feel
right. If you feel like moving, move. Comments like "Oh, yes"
and "That feels great" are good to hear.

⁞63⁞

Hum Job

Humming while using your mouth on various
parts of your lover's body can add a light, silly, and often
erotic tone. Depending on the situation, humming certain
songs can be fun. "Happy Birthday" has a cult following.

:64:

Getting Spicy

It's reliably reported to me that fellatio can be enhanced by using cinnamon oil as a penis lubricant. (Be sure you both read the section on menthol Tricks before attempting this Trick.) The woman who told me about this Trick remarked, "There are so many different ways to give head that it just blows me away!" ⌘ Note: Quite a few people find straight cinnamon oil too intense. You can dilute the oil with something tamer, or try cinnamon leaf oil, a milder version.

:65:

Bite and Breathe

Take a sensitive part of your lover's body into your mouth, lightly bite it, then breathe long, slow, sensuous breaths in and out while you hold it in your teeth. Cross-reference this Trick with Vampire Attack #2 (Trick #34).

.66.

Pepper-Upper

It's also reliably reported to me, from more than one source, that both masturbating and fellating a man can be enhanced by using peppermint oil. One caution: A single dose of peppermint oil can take several minutes to be fully felt, and the sensation tends to come on all at once. Therefore, as when experimenting with any "hot sauce" or when with a new lover, start with a very small amount and wait several minutes – at least five – before adding more. ⌘ Holding a peppermint candy in your mouth while performing fellatio can also be intense. (It also might be ever-so-slightly dangerous. See the "Menthol Tricks" chapter for more information before using peppermint. The same principles apply.)

.67.

Lube Early, Lube Often

In any situation where you're using lubricant, such as masturbation or anal intercourse, it's wise to add more *before* you need to. Things may become quite unpleasant before more lube is actually requested.

Invited Guests are Always Welcome

This is a subtle point, so please pay attention.
When caressing a woman's genitals, don't be too quick to
insert your fingers. Keep stroking her exterior until you are
"invited in." The person who taught me about this Trick said,
"Let her contractions pull you in."

Hot Tip

It's reliably reported to me that condom usage
can be made more pleasurable for the man if
one drop of water-based lubricant is placed in its
reservoir tip before it's applied.

"Freeze!"

You are not to move or make any sounds
while your lover "does" you.

·71·

Lid Lick

Several people reported that they could reliably
arouse their lovers by licking their eyelids.

·72·

Fine Tune Your Touch

It's been repeatedly reported to me that many men find
women's caresses too light, and that many women find men's
caresses too heavy. (Especially at first.)

·73·

Ice Cube Trick #2

An ice cube can be used to good effect on breasts, nipples,
and other body areas. Inserting a cube into the vagina and/or
anus (not too big, we don't want frostbite   here) is a
reliable gasp-producer. Melt the frost, and
any sharp edges, off the cube first, either
by holding it in your fist or by running it
briefly under a stream of tap water. ⌘
One experienced lady told me that ice
cubes work particularly well on a hot day.
Footnote: Ice plus body heat plus time
equals water. I suggest keeping a small towel
handy if you do this Trick.

•••• 74 ••••

Hooker's Trick #4

One professional I interviewed told me that both she and her clients enjoy it when she undresses them. The usual pattern, she pointed out, is for the man to undress the woman and then to undress himself. Many men have never been undressed by a woman. They therefore find the experience, particularly if her eagerness makes her a bit "rough" while she does it, exciting and intense.

•••• 75 ••••

Don't Share Your Toys

We live in a time when having multiple partners is considerably more risky than it used to be. We also live in a time when many of us have multiple partners. ⌘ One way to cope with the health concerns of having multiple partners is to have sex toys for use on only that person. This can apply to vibrators, dildoes, and other equipment. If possible, leaving "their" equipment at their house helps make certain they are the only person that equipment is used on.

.76.
But If You Do

Safe sex practices also apply to adult toys,
particularly those used for penetration.
If you have a vibrator or dildo that you use on more than one
person, cover it with a condom before using it,
particularly before using it for insertion.

.77.
Clean Them After Each Use

If you have toys that you use on more than one person, it's
important to clean them thoroughly after each use, even if you
did use a condom. Ordinary soap and water, 70% rubbing
alcohol, betadine-type solutions, 30% hydrogen peroxide, and
other materials can be used. A solution of one part bleach to
nine parts water is very popular. ⌘ Different toys need
different types of cleaning. Latex and leather items can be
harmed if cleaned in the wrong way. The
store where you bought the item or a sex
information line can help advise you. ⌘
One tip: After you've cleaned a toy,
make sure it's given adequate time to dry
(such as overnight) before using it again.
Drying in and of itself kills many bugs.

78
Wonderful Wipes

Diaper wipes can be bought in plastic bottles. They contain disinfectants to kill the AIDS virus and other bugs. These are excellent for removing condoms and general clean-up.

79
Hot Sex

Temperature play, in various forms, is a favorite oral sex Trick. One of the simplest, yet absolutely most effective, variants on this is to simply keep a cup of hot liquid by the bed. This can be coffee, tea, or plain hot water. One of my most informed sources of information regarding oral sex said that, of all her different methods, this was the simplest, easiest to control, and evoked the most response.

80
Fronts and Backs

One of my highly reliable sources tells me that people who have very sensitive, erotic nipples probably also have very sensitive, erotic lower backs.

:81:
I Got Rhythm

One playful lady told me that her lovers really enjoy it if,
during intercourse, she keeps time to the
music by squeezing her vaginal muscles.

:82:
All The World's A Stage

One Trick to make erotic entertainment, such as watching
videos, more intense and satisfying is to enjoy such
entertainment in a place where you don't normally have sex.
This may be as simple as watching the video in the living room
instead of the bedroom or as elaborate as going out to a strip
club. Changing the environment is a reliable tension builder.

:83:
Look, Don't Touch

Another reliable tension builder while
watching erotic entertainment is to
avoid touching each other.
Sit in separate chairs, out of each other's
reach, and let the charge build.

•••
:84:
•••
Value Received

In this game, one of you is "hired" by the other for sex. The "hooker" must do, within wide limits, whatever the "Trick" wants, and the price for various acts can be negotiated. The benefit for the client is that they get "serviced" in exactly the way they want. The benefit for the sex worker is that they get paid. (Make certain you keep this game free of real deprivation or manipulation, and remember to always be "professionally polite" with each other. No name-calling or other put-downs.) ⌘ One final point: Just as the customer gets to keep the pleasure they received, so does the hooker get to keep the money they have rightfully earned.

•••
:85:
•••
In The Spotlight

A lot of men like to closely examine a woman's body, and they rarely get a chance to do that. Darken the room, give him a very small flashlight, and let him examine you – especially, although perhaps not right at the beginning, your pussy. ⌘ Don't worry too much about your body not being perfect. The smallness of the flashlight makes the examination about your parts, not about you as a whole – and you can wear a (highly adjustable) negligee if you want.

•86•

Hair Heaven

If you have long hair, you can use it to whip your lover. Your hair can feel wonderfully sensuous on their chest, back, and other body areas. One caution: Keep clear of their face. A lock of your hair across their eyes can, to say the least, spoil the mood. Swing your hair back and forth, sideways, and in other directions. (Don't hurt your neck.) If it's long enough, hold it in your hand and use it. Women who have long hair can often combine this Trick well with her-on-top intercourse.

•87•

Make A Snake

Straighten out your hands as you might do while praying and hold his penis in between them. Then rub your hands back and forth, as you might do when handling cooking dough or modeling clay. ✹ This Trick has great variability. You can change - among other things - how fast you rub your hands, when you start and stop, whether or not to include the sensitive head of his penis, and both what type and how much (if any) lubricant you use while doing this. ✹ If you're feeling like being extra nice to him, take the head of his penis in your mouth while you apply this stroke to the shaft.

•••• 88 ••••
Search and Rescue

Pubic hair, as well as hair from other areas,
occasionally ends up in your mouth, and can be a major
irritation. I've had excellent results in removing such
hair using an ordinary toothbrush.

•••• 89 ••••
Pushing The Right Button

Does she like direct stimulation or indirect stimulation of her
clitoris? Does she like lots of pressure or very little pressure? Is
one side of her clit more sensitive than the other? (This is not
rare.)

•••• 90 ••••
Slow and Steady Wins the Race

Stay with what is already working. Don't intensify whatever
you're doing as her orgasm nears. Such a change often works
well with a male partner, but not so with a woman. Even slight
changes often don't work well. (This was reported to me by
considerably more than one person.)

∴91∴

Don't Just Lie Back, Feedback!

Many men feel, and it's often true, that their sexual touch is not really wanted by the woman involved. They feel it is often something she is tolerating, sometimes with the thought of getting something in return. Therefore, a woman can do much to put a man at ease by reassuring him that she does indeed welcome his touch - assuming, of course, that is indeed the case. If it's not, they need to talk, probably outside the bedroom. ⌘ If she does genuinely want him, she can often use words very creatively. Many men love hearing encouraging phrases such as "harder," "deeper," and "take me."

·92·

Up and Down #1

This is a Trick for masturbating a man that requires a bit of coordination at first, but is very powerful once you master it.

⌘ If you watch a man masturbate, you'll see that he typically uses one hand to stroke his penis in an up and down motion. All well and good. ⌘ You can add some variety and spice to this by using one of your hands only for upstrokes and the other only for downstrokes. One way to learn how to do this is to have him lie on his back while you sit or kneel (whatever is comfortable) between his legs. Lightly grasp the base of his penis with your right hand and gently hold its tip with your left. (This Trick usually works best when both his penis and your hands are well-lubricated.) ⌘ Stroke upwards with your right hand. When your right hand passes "through" the fingers of your left and off the top of his penis, grasp his penis with your left hand and slide down its shaft. While your left hand is sliding down, move your right hand slightly away and back to the base of his penis. After your left hand slides down and away, repeat the upstroke with your right hand. ⌘ While the upstroke is going on, your left hand returns to the head of the penis so its stroke can be repeated. Both hands move in oval-like shapes, and both move in either a clockwise or counter-clockwise direction. Of course, that direction can be reversed. Use a slow speed at first, then increase and/or vary the speed as appropriate.

:93:
Up and Down #2

Lubricate both hands. Grasp his cock with both hands and hold
it like you would a baseball bat. Keep your lower hand still
while you slide your upper hand up and off the head of his
penis. As your upper hand slides off, raise your lower hand up
and off. Your upper then returns to the base and repeats the
journey, and so does the lower. Vary the speed and pressure of
your hands as seems right. Experiment. This sensation makes
the man feel as if he were constantly withdrawing from a
vagina. It's can be very powerful. ⌘ A simple, yet also
quite intense variant of this technique is to move your hands
one over the other in a downward motion, so it feels to him
like he's constantly entering a vagina. Of course, you can also
do one stroke for a while, and then the other.

94.

Do The Twist

The lower edge of the tip of a man's penis (the corona) is very sensitive to touch, perhaps the most sensitive part of all. Tongues, fingers, and other items can be used to good effect here. ⌘ One excellent way to make masturbation more intense and pleasurable is to give your hand a light twist as it passes over the corona in the down-to-up direction. To illustrate, make your hand into a not-too-tight fist with your thumb on top of your index finger. Hold this in front of you so that your thumb is pointed straight ahead. Now turn your fist so that it's facing palm-up and slide your thumb slightly toward the floor. You have just done the basic twist. ⌘ Use this twist lightly (too much pressure may spoil it) and you will dramatically improve the quality of the hand jobs you give.

•95•
When All Else Fails...

Condoms, contraceptive gels, and similar devices often come with a small instruction sheet. The information in this packet is essential. Smart people take this sheet out and read it long before the information it contains will be needed. Don't let your existing level of education lead you into thinking you don't need to read the sheet.
New information often appears here: I once made a terribly embarrassing mistake by not reading the directions that came with a box of "Mentor" condoms.

•96•
A Movable Fist

This Trick is useful when masturbating or performing oral sex on your partner. Make one hand into a fist and place it just behind their genitals. The thumb side should point forward and the little finger side should point to their rear. Thrust upward against their body. The strength of this thrust can be anywhere from very light to very heavy, depending on what works for both of you. The strength can also be varied. As an extra touch, you can vibrate your fist.

97.

Breathe Together

Match your breathing to your partner's. Doing so often
increases the intensity of the experience for both of you.
Matching your breathing also brings you into the here and now;
again, that makes things more intense. You don't necessarily
have to tell your partner that you are doing this; just do it and
see what happens. Matching your breathing to your partner's
as they approach and go through orgasm can be particularly
intense. ⌘ Note: Exercises in which you match your
breathing to your partner's are taught in many sexual/spiritual
practices such as tantra and quodoushka.

98.

Thumb Fun

Encircle the penis just below its head with your
thumb and forefinger and your thumb on the back of the
penis. Rotate your index finger up and over the
head of the penis and then back to where you started,
keeping your thumb stationary. This can be an
intense, highly pleasurable Trick.

99
Sexual Heeling

Place the heel of your hand on her vaginal area
with her clitoris at the bottom center of your palm,
then vibrate your hand.

100
A-one And A-two

I've watched many lesbian videos, and interviewed many
lesbians about how they have sex. When one inserts her fingers
into her partner's vagina, it seems the usual practice is for her
to use two fingers; not one, not three or four, but two.

101
A-one and A-two and A-three

A variant on the "two finger" approach
mentioned above is the "cocked pistol"
technique in which you insert your first
two fingers into her, then arch your
thumb back "hitch-hiker" style, and
thrust in until your thumb rests against
her clitoris. You can use a variety of
thrusting and twisting motions in this
position. You can also vibrate your entire hand.

102

Hooker's Trick #5

One time-honored cat house specialty is the Creme de Menthe blow job. Its unusual color, minty odor, and hot/cool sensation (along with the regular benefits) have helped prostitutes pay the rent for many years. ⌘ You put a teaspoon of the green variety in your mouth and then touch his penis to your lips. Open your mouth very slightly and let the liquor out. Make sure he can see the green spread. ⌘ Once the green has spread over his cock, open your mouth until it's open slightly wider than his cock - a bit farther than you usually would. Lower your mouth way down over his penis, with your lips close to but not touching it, and blow out. This creates a hot, astonishing sensation. ⌘ After that, with your lips still not quite touching, suck in air (rather forcefully) as you raise your head up the shaft of the penis. This creates an exquisite, cool sensation. Repeat as desired. ⌘ Footnote #1: The liquor also feels good on his testicles. ⌘ Footnote #2: You can also fan his liquor-coated cock with a pretty, feathered fan to good effect. ⌘ Warning: My source for this Trick cautioned me that the alcohol is likely to burn too much for it to work well during cunnilingus.

103

The Trident

When masturbating her, try placing your thumb on her clitoris, your first three fingers in her vagina, and your little finger in her anus. ⌘ Major Safety Note: Make sure your fingernails are short and smooth, especially the nail on your little finger. Test this by scraping your nails against the inside of your opposite forearm. If doing so feels sharp, rough, or jagged, file them down. In a worst case situation, a jagged nail could pierce the intestinal wall, so be careful here. She should never feel any sharp pain in her anus. (A latex glove might make this Trick safer and more comfortable for both people. For more information see "A Few Don'ts Regarding Tricks" chapter.)

104

Slow and Spready

Many men have difficulty reaching orgasm if their legs are spread apart. If you're feeling mischievous, "make him earn it" by sitting between his legs while you use your hands and mouth.

105
Give Him A Wring

Grip his cock between your two (probably well-lubricated) hands. Your uppermost hand should include the top of his penis in your grip. Twist your hands together until your thumbs are pointing in the same direction, then twist your hands apart until your thumbs are pointing in parallel-but-opposite directions. Repeat this stroke, varying speed and grip strength, as appropriate.

106
Women and Touch #1

A woman who teaches classes for women on strip-tease dancing told me that she is often approached by men who want to learn how to do that. She replies that whereas men tend to have a high visual component to their sexuality (a fact that made Hugh Hefner rich), women tend to have a high tactile component. She tells them, "Before you learn how to strip, learn how to give a really good massage."

:107:

Women and Touch #2

She went on to say that many men don't understand how
"touch conscious" women are. "Don't aggressively touch
women," she said. "Touching women too soon panics them."
She specifically mentioned putting an arm around a woman's
shoulder before she's ready for that as a common error men
make. She went on to add, "I hate it when a man is calling me
pet names within ten minutes of meeting me, or when he pats
my hand while he's shaking it." ⌘ Her final point about this
area was that women who work in jobs that involve touching
or being touched by others, particularly women who take care
of small children, may be "touched out" by the end of the
day. The arrival of one more person into her day who
wants to touch and be touched can drive her nuts.
A smart lover will give her as much time by herself as she
needs before any more touching.

:108:

Face Up To It

Our face is one of the most personal
parts of our bodies. Touching someone on
the face is therefore an act of intimate
affection (or domination).
Provided they welcome it, a caress on your lover's face
is a sensuous, caring act.

109

The Couple That Reads Together, Succeeds Together

While men tend to be visual and women tend to be tactile, both genders tend to be quite fond of the written word. Therefore, it can be great fun, and highly arousing, to either read erotica together or to read it out loud to each other.

110

Latex Isn't Forever

Condoms have a shelf life. Any condom over two years old is at greatly increased risk for breaking at highly inopportune moments. Also, heat breaks them down even faster. Keep them out of your wallet!

111

Bridge Game

One mischievous young lady reported that she has had excellent results licking the area at the top of the nose and between the eyes. As she put it, "You can never tell where an erogenous zone is going to be."

112

Close But No Cigar

If your lover has a particular spot that they like to have licked or caressed, try doing so very close to but *not quite* on that spot - except perhaps occasionally. This Trick will make them take longer to reach their orgasm, but they will likely have a much stronger, more powerful orgasm when it does finally happen. As a variant, you can do the "not quite on target" until they get close to coming, then - if you're feeling benevolent - switch to the target itself, thus earning their gratitude.

113

Keep Your Eye On The...

Watch your lover's face while they watch yours. You can make eye contact, perhaps focusing in on one particular eye, or simply watch their whole face. Don't stare or glare at them. Instead, think "soft, bedroom eyes." Don't feel you have to react to their gaze in any particular way. Just be there together, softly looking at each other.

//

114

Don't Ask

Many of us become somewhat non-verbal as
our arousal increases. Therefore, asking someone if they like
what you're doing can be distracting once things go beyond a
certain point. It can break the magic spell the two of you are
creating. Instead of outright asking, pay attention to their
breathing, their muscle tone, any sounds they make, and so
forth. As you get to know your lover, you'll get better at
figuring out if what you're doing is working. I've had lovers tell
me, "Just go ahead. I'll let you know if I have a problem. If
you don't hear from me, just assume everything is all right."
This was wonderful, very freeing, advice to hear.

115

Get Happy, Not Pregnant

If you're worried about the possibility of pregnancy, keep in
mind that your partner may not want to have vaginal
intercourse so much as they want to have an orgasm - with
your help. Skillful use of your hand and/or mouth may help
resolve the situation. (I can tell you that, in my own case,
many is the time I would have happily accepted that solution.)

116

Nipples: No Two Are Alike

One of the things I have learned over the years is how variable women are in their response to different types of nipple stimulation. For some women, nipple stimulation is hardly erotic at all – perhaps even a turn-off. On the other end of the spectrum are women who easily reach orgasm by nipple stimulation alone. As one put it, "It's like there's a hot wire running directly from my nipple to my clit." Most women, in my experience, are somewhere in the middle. ⌘ Some women like only the lightest of touches on their nipples, others relish stimulation up to and including strong pinches and bites. (If you play with such strong stimulation, always start slowly and lightly and gradually build up to the stronger stuff, particularly if this is a new partner or new Trick – and be careful not to break the skin.) Some like constant stimulation, others like pauses. ⌘ Stimulation that works well on a woman's right nipple sometimes doesn't work all that well on her left. Also, the type of stimulation that works can vary with her menstrual cycle. A woman's nipples are often exceptionally sensitive just before or during her period. Stimulation she enjoyed two weeks ago may now be too intense or painful. ⌘ While what caught my attention was how variably different women respond to the same type of nipple stimulation, I need to point out that exactly the same is true of men's nipples, and of other body areas in both genders.

117

Ball Pull

While using your hand and/or mouth to pleasure his penis,
encircle the top of his scrotum with the thumb and forefinger
of your other hand. Squeeze this ring together until it's snug
and his testicles are "trapped" below it. Slowly and lightly pull
down until the skin of his scrotum is pulled tight over his
testicles. Lightly pull just a little more for about five seconds
while you continue to pleasure his penis. Then release the pull
(but keep your hand in place). Closely watch his face,
breathing, and body for a reaction. Repeat, varying the
strength and the length of the pull while you mix it with large
amounts of pleasure. ⌘ Men will vary considerably in
their reaction to this Trick. Some will find it so painful as to be
a turn-off and want you to stop. Others will like it and want
you to continue. Some will *really* like it and want you to pull
down harder. (Don't get carried away. This Trick,
carried to extremes, could damage him.) Getting feedback
from him on how long and how hard he wants the pull to
be is an excellent idea.

118

TesTickles

Once you have his balls "trapped" as described in Trick #116, you can lick, caress, and lightly scratch the tightly stretched skin over them to excellent effect.

119

Stroke Their Aura

During sex, you usually start with very light touches and strokes and then progress to heavier strokes. As a variant, once you have reached the "heavy strokes" phase, have your partner lie still and focus your strokes on a particular part of their body, preferably one they can see. Start with your strokes quite firm, and gradually lighten them until you are touching them with only the lightest of touches. Then gradually withdraw your hand from actual physical contact with them and caress the "aura" surrounding that part of their body. The results can literally feel electrifying.

120

The Prisoner

Order your partner to stand up with their hands behind their head, fingers laced together, and their legs spread somewhat apart. Keep their knees slightly bent. (They may faint if they stand too long with their knees locked; this is well-known to soldiers and others who must stand in one place for any length of time.) ⌘ Now go to work on them. Caress them, masturbate them, give them head, tease them, and so on, and so on, and so on. Don't let them come too quickly. When they finally do, the results can be earth-moving.

121

Pin and Win

Normally, when you lick a nipple, it moves back and forth under your tongue, and some sensation is therefore lost. To prevent this, spread your index and middle finger slightly apart and place them on either side. (Don't push down on the chest so much that you cause pain.)
Once they're in place, spread them even farther apart. Your lover's nipple may noticeably bulge out as you do this. Now, with the nipple in this exposed and immobile position, apply your tongue and notice the difference.

122

Jilling Off

Many of the male masturbation strokes described in
this book can be equally well applied – with, of course, the
necessary adjustments – to the clitoris.

123

The Old In and Out

This Trick works best if you position yourself so you can see
each other's faces. As one of you breathes out, the other
breathes in. Continue this "opposite breathing" pattern while
you, if possible, maintain eye contact. The woman who told
me of this Trick went on to say, "It gets hot fast." ⌘
Subpoint: Make sure your breath is fresh!

124

A Sound Idea

If you feel like making a sound during sex,
by all means go ahead and make it
(assuming, of course, that doing so
won't wake the kids or otherwise disturb
anybody else within earshot). You don't
have to make a big production out of this,
but if a sound feels like emerging, let it come out
naturally. Such sounds may be a turn-on to your lover. The
lady who told me of this Trick also mentioned, "It gives them a
real clear clue that what they're doing is working."

///.

125

Knee Whee

The backs on the knees, perhaps particularly in
women, are often a highly erotic part of the body. I've had it
reported to me by more than source that stimulation here
often corresponds in intensity with direct stimulation of the
clitoris. One woman told me she could reach a powerful,
trembling orgasm by having the backs of her knees licked.

Menthol Tricks

Menthol creates intense sensations when applied to the skin. These sensations are usually felt either as heat or as "chilled heat." Menthol-containing products can be used to spice up fellatio (cough drops) or as a male masturbation lubricant (chest rubs and arthritis creams). Their labels will tell you whether or not they contain menthol.

Menthol-containing products are not designed, intended, or recommended for internal use. Using them in combination with fellatio, cunnilingus, vibrators, dildoes, vaginal intercourse, or anal intercourse is not recommended. I have heard of some lunatics attempting to use them for those activities, but in most cases such usage was more painful than they could stand. These substances can also upset the natural biological balance of such areas.

A very small amount of menthol can, in some cases, be applied to the clitoris to make female masturbation more intense, but please be careful. Remember, it's not intended for internal use, and it feels much "hotter" on mucous membranes. Ladies, I suggest you try this on your own before involving another person.

Menthol-containing cough drops might be used during cunnilingus, but please note the above warnings carefully.

Menthol must be used cautiously. Whereas other Tricks are spices, menthol qualifies as red hot pepper. Using a *very* small amount may spice things up nicely. Too much can cause genuine agony.

Start slowly and with small amounts when using a menthol-containing cream. It's often wise to "dilute" it with another lubricant. Never use the extra-strength brand of anything until you've used the regular strength brand successfully several times. Understand that gels can be *much* hotter than creams.

Menthol may take up to five minutes for the effects of a given "dose" to be fully felt, so take your time about adding more. One dose is usually felt for about twenty minutes, but this can vary considerably from person to person and from product to product. Menthol applied to the scrotum is usually felt sooner and feels hotter than menthol applied to the penis.

A Few Cautions

There is a very slight possibility of your choking if you perform fellatio while holding a foreign object, such as an ice cube, peppermint candy, or cough drop, in your mouth. Therefore, never attempt such a Trick while even slightly intoxicated, and make sure you know how to do the Heimlich maneuver on yourself. (Using the back of a chair helps a lot.)

Chest rubs and arthritis creams are oil-based, and thus should be avoided in situations that require condoms

If you use a menthol-containing cream to masturbate a man, a considerable amount will get on your hand as well as his cock. Because the skin of your hand is much thicker than the skin of his penis, it may take time for you to feel this. "Burning Hands Syndrome" can develop an hour or more after the session. You might therefore wear latex or vinyl gloves when playing with menthol.

Be careful about combining menthol with abrasion. Skin that has been scraped, such as by fingernails, will be considerably less able to tolerate menthol.

Menthol leaves a distinct smell in the air. It's a good idea to use it only in well-ventilated areas if the lingering smell might be a problem.

"Overdoses"

It's easy to add more menthol, but it's very difficult to remove what you've already applied. If you do have a "menthol overdose," you can usually wash it off by using cold running water and lots of soap. Applying large amounts of shampoo and then washing it off works especially well. Very liberal amounts of the astringent called witch hazel also wash it off. (Your drugstore carries it.) You can also "cool things down" by rubbing on generous amounts of petroleum jelly or an oil-based cream. (Be sure you don't use a chest rub!) I haven't personally tested it, but I'm told that cold cream works well. Physically cooling the area seems to help.

You might consider deliberately creating a menthol overdose in order to test these various cool-down methods. That way, in an actual "emergency," you'll have a clearer idea of what works (and what doesn't). Understand that different people may respond better to different cooling methods.

Don't combine menthol play with bondage until you, your partner, and the substance in question are well acquainted. A menthol overdose is especially likely to occur during the first one or two times you use it with a new partner. If they get overdosed and need to run to the shower, they'll need to be able to run there *now*.

I don't recommend using menthol with a new partner unless they (and you) are already highly experienced in its use. It's too easy for things to go wrong and perhaps harm your budding relationship. Use this only for self-play or with someone you already know well. It would be a good idea to use a particular lubricant on yourself several times before you ask a partner to use it on you.

Because menthol "burns" for about twenty minutes after being applied (some brands burn longer), and because this feeling may be seriously unpleasant if no longer accompanied by sexual arousal, it's both wise and compassionate to wait for its sensations to fade to a very low level before bringing your partner to orgasm.

As you can see, menthol usage is one of the more serious Tricks. Just understand that it's not a toy. Use menthol improperly and you'll regret it. Use it properly and you can add an enormous amount of intensity and pleasure to your lovemaking.

Madonna/Whore Complex

Sex is still not a valued and honored part of life for many men. Too many men still see sex as dirty and degrading, and therefore so is any woman who engages in it. Such beliefs have given rise to that old saying among men "there are girls you fuck and girls you marry." (My informed sources tell me a highly similar saying exists among many women.)

It strikes me as no accident that a woman named Madonna is becoming both famous and infamous by running around our culture "acting like a whore." Far, far too many men desperately want a sexual woman, yet panic at the sight of one.

Many men desperately want a woman to be sexual with them, yet lose respect for the woman if she does. This reminds me of the story of the man who repeatedly begged his reluctant girlfriend to perform oral sex on him. When she finally obliged, he beat her up "for being a cocksucker." That is serious craziness.

Guys, we have got to make up our minds how we feel about sex. We have got to get clear within ourselves as to whether we see sex as a basically good thing or a basically bad thing.

One thing is certain: if you continue to see sex as a bad thing, yet want women to do it with you, then fewer and fewer women will tolerate being involved with you. I suggest that you either change your thinking or get good at jerking off.

Attention Ladies: One of my most highly informed (female) sources suggests that if your boyfriend or husband asks you to share in sexual entertainment with him, such as going to a strip club, it's wise to accept his offer and go with him. His offer may be a sign that he's beginning to let go of his madonna/whore thinking, and that's something you should encourage.

Sex, Risk, Probability, and Political Correctness

Having sex has always been dangerous. Vaginal intercourse almost always involves at least a minimal risk of unwanted pregnancy. Throughout history the chance of picking up an incurable, fatal disease was often present. (The big specter used to be syphilis; now, of course, it's AIDS.) And let's not even begin to get into how introducing sex into a previously nonsexual relationship can cause massive social uproar.

About ten years ago, having sex suddenly became a lot more dangerous than it had been for quite some time. The re-emergence of a fatal, incurable, sexually transmitted disease has once again changed the very fabric of how we live – and will continue to change it for decades.

People want to know how they can have sex and yet protect themselves. Various authorities respond with this or that regimen. Some regimens are excellent; some are a crime.

What I don't think is made clear enough to those seeking information is that essentially all of this is a matter of probabilities. No complication occurs 100% of the time, and no protective measure is 100% effective. It's all a case of shifting the odds. Granted, in many cases the odds can and should be shifted, but we need to make it clearer to people than we do that it's still a matter of probability. We see some signs of this by the emergence of the term "safer sex" to replace the somewhat misleading "safe sex."

"Political Correctness" has helped complicate things. Early in the AIDS crisis, when the modes of disease transmission were less well understood than they are today, various authorities advocated nothing less than "total body fluid isolation" rules. Bedrooms all over America began to resemble hospital "protective isolation" wards.

Today, certain practices – oral sex, in particular – are believed to be considerably less risky than previously thought. Unfortunately, no authority can recommend less than total body fluid isolation without becoming vulnerable to accusations of reckless irresponsibility by their more conservative peers. They therefore keep silent even though they might like to speak up. Taking a politically incorrect position, even if the data supports it, can ruin a career.

And, to be fair, these more conservative peers have some merit in what they say. While the odds seem sharply against it, you most definitely can become infected with the AIDS virus by performing only a single act of oral sex on an HIV+ person. Some authorities even assert you risk infection if this person performs oral sex on you.

(By the way, it also now seems that unprotected anal sex is considerably *more* risky than previously thought.)

Add into this mess that the usual medical experiments to study infectious disease cannot, for ethical reasons, be conducted, plus the new strains of virus which are emerging, and you have a genuinely murky situation. For example, we know that nonoxynol-9 kills the AIDS virus, and there's reason to believe that people who use only nonoxynol-9 to protect themselves against AIDS have a noticeably lower rate of becoming infected than those who use nothing, but no truly accurate estimates of exactly how much protection nonoxynol-9 provides seem to exist. Furthermore, finding out may be impossible.

As a finishing touch, add in the numerous personal, economic, social, political, and religious influences. The situation's clarity now drops to near zero.

So what *do* you do? Stop and think. Ask various authorities for information. Ask them (and yourself) how reliable and complete is the information on which they're basing their decisions and recommendations. Be sure to consider any hidden agendas, particularly any political or religious agendas, this authority may have.

Have you had an AIDS antibody test? This is one of the most responsible steps you can take. If you've had any unsafe contacts, have you had a test since then? Do you really understand what information such a test does and does not provide?

Has the person you're considering having sex with had such a test? How reliable is their answer likely to be? Many, many people will lie right to your face if doing so will get you to have sex with them, particularly if their chance seems close.

As it stands now, masturbating your partner seems very safe – and a skillfully administered hand job can be one of the most intense sexual experiences possible. Combine it with a lubricant containing nonoxynol-9 and the absence of any openings in the skin on your hands or their genitals and you're almost as safe as you can get. While I imagine it's happened in a few cases, I personally have never heard of anyone getting infected or becoming pregnant from using a lubricant containing nonoxynol-9 to masturbate or be masturbated by their partner.

Oral sex seems "relatively" safe. Pregnancy is almost unheard of, and it's been reliably documented that saliva neutralizes the AIDS virus. Still, some risk is involved. Please understand clearly that gonorrhea, syphilis, herpes, and other diseases can be transmitted this way (in both directions). Furthermore, the risk of getting AIDS, while small, does exist.

Vaginal sex is, of course, definitely risky. The risk of unplanned pregnancy and sexually transmitted disease is almost always present. Please be very, very careful about how and with whom you have vaginal intercourse.

Receptive anal sex seems to be, in terms of getting AIDS, the riskiest form of sex you can have these days. (The active role is not risk-free either.) A physician told me that the odds of getting infected by having a single act of unprotected, receptive anal sex with an HIV+ partner were a staggering one chance in three.

As you can see, sex involves more risk than ever before. Make sure you've had a recent antibody test. Pick your partners carefully; remember, even normally honest people will lie, particularly during "the heat of passion," if doing so will get you to have sex with them.

Choosing which acts you'll participate in definitely helps shift the odds in your favor. Using nonoxynol-9 also shifts them. A condom, provided it's used properly, adds considerable protection. Dental dams and latex gloves play crucial roles.

There is no such thing as risk-free sex. Still, as with driving a car, flying a plane, or swimming, you can reduce the odds to a level where most people consider the risk acceptable. You, of course, must decide where that level is for you. (Whatever you do, don't let another person make this decision for you.) Remember, nothing is 100% dangerous and nothing is 100% safe. Also remember that VD clinics, pregnancy crisis centers, and AIDS wards are filled with people who insisted on blinding themselves to the full extent of the risks they took.

We live in an age where sixty seconds of clear thinking about what is proper sexual behavior for you can add sixty years to your life.

Lubricants – Advantages, Disadvantages, and Dangers

I decided not to include sex toys such as vibrators and so on in this book. Doing so would have made it much larger, and made the audience narrower. I have dealt with such topics in another book, "Sex Toy Tricks: More Than 125 Ways to Accessorize Good Sex."

Lubricants, creams, gels, and so forth are one category of "adjuncts" to erotic play that I will discuss. In addition to adding (often very considerably) to the pleasure of those involved, lubricants can be used to help prevent pregnancy, relieve vaginal dryness, and help reduce the spread of sexually transmitted diseases, so they merit discussion in this book. Some menthol-containing lubricants cause a distinctly "hot" sensation when applied to the genitals, so some people use them for erotic play. I've discussed such lubricants in their own chapter.

Almost all lubricants can be grouped into one of two basic categories: Oil-based and water-based. Oil-based lubricants generally stay "slippery" considerably longer than water-based lubricants. Unfortunately, these days they have a major, life-threatening property: Oil-based lubricants rapidly dissolve latex. Therefore, any latex product that gets smeared with an oil-based lubricant will fall apart much sooner than it otherwise would. (Note: there is a growing range of new safer sex products made of materials other than latex. Polyurethane condoms, and gloves of nitrile and vinyl, are a tremendous boon to people with latex allergies, and are also oil-proof.)

If you are in a situation where you need to use a latex condom or other latex protective device, keep oil-based lubricants away from it.

The single most important thing you need to know about a lubricant is whether it is water-based or oil-based. If you are not 100% sure, you would be very wise to assume that it's oil-based and treat it accordingly.

The next most important thing you need to know about a lubricant is whether or not it contains nonoxynol-9. Some people believe that only water-based lubricants contain nonoxynol-9 and, therefore, believe that if they buy a lubricant containing nonoxynol-9 they are automatically buying a water-based lubricant. This is simply not true. While most oil-based lubricants do not contain nonoxynol-9, I know of at least two different brands that do. Water-based lubricants usually state that fact plainly. Read the label carefully.

If you can, find out what percentage of nonoxynol-9 is present. Ordinary lubricants typically contain about 1% (and usually don't state the percentage on the label). Contraceptive gels tend to run 2% or a bit higher.

I have long believed that nonoxynol-9 should be used far more widely than it is now. Most people can use it with no problems, and it contributes a lot toward helping to fight unplanned pregnancy and sexually transmitted disease.

Water-based lubes can be used with condoms and other devices, but they tend to dry out and get "sticky" much more quickly than oil-based lubes. Therefore, smart players keep a small supply of water close by. This can either be something like a "finger bowl" or a separate bottle just for holding water. Sometimes the lubricant-containing bottle and the water-containing bottle are glued or taped together so one doesn't get quite so easily lost. One caution: When you need to add water, add only a very few drops. You can, for all practical purposes, wash the lubricant (and its benefits) away if you add too much water. "Every now and then" add more lubricant instead of adding more water.

Supplemental Thought: Your saliva can also be used to help loosen up the lubricant, and contact with saliva reduces the infectivity of the AIDS virus. Welcome this extra protection, but definitely don't rely on it.

Another Supplemental Thought: A physician told me some evidence exists that the use of any lubricant might (repeat, might) reduce the possibility of passing on a sexually transmitted disease. The thinking is that, because lubricants reduce the amount of "wear and tear" on the body parts involved, fewer breaks in the skin get created, and thus the probability of at least some forms of disease transmission is reduced. (Other bugs, of course, go right through intact skin with no problem at all.) As with the information about saliva noted above, welcome this extra protection, but absolutely do not rely on it.

A visit to your local drugstore, adult bookstore, or erotic boutique will help acquaint you with, among others, such names as Astroglide, Liquid Silk, Probe, Slippery Stuff, KY Jelly, PrePair, ForPlay, and Wet. (You should also look over their selection of condoms, contraceptive gels, spermicidal suppositories, and so forth.)

Your local drugstore may also have some additional, unexpected treasures. A liquefying cleanser called Albolene has enjoyed a semi-underground following for years as an excellent lubricant for erotic play, particularly masturbation. At some sex parties, you get a discount on your admission fee if you bring a jar – a sort of BYOA situation. One caution: Albolene is oil-based and doesn't contain nonoxynol-9, so choose when you use it carefully.

Other "non-traditional" lubricants include Johnson's Baby Magic Lotion, Crisco, coconut oil (one of my favorites), vegetable oil, and petroleum jelly. These all share Albolene's limits.

A carefully chosen lubricant can add considerable safety and pleasure to your erotic play. Make sure you clearly understand the advantages and disadvantages of each type.

Nightstand Supplies

Assuming most of your sexual activity takes place in your bed, it helps to keep the following supplies nearby, possibly in your nightstand.

1. Something non-alcoholic to drink. This can help relieve the sometimes considerable thirst people can work up. If you're not wild about having someone come in your mouth, but willing to let them, keeping a strongly flavored liquid close by can help quickly wash the taste away.

2. A music source that requires little attention. Auto-reverse and repeat features are useful. While tastes vary, many people prefer instrumental music. Lyrics can distract, and they're often about unpleasant topics.

3. Soft, small towels kept nearby help with clean-up. (Many hookers refer to these as "trick towels.") If you leave a large wet spot, consider placing a very absorbent towel under you before things get serious.

4. Lubricants make life easier. Make sure they're in containers that can be easily opened with slippery hands. If you use water-soluble lubricants, also keep a small "finger bowl" of water handy so you can add a few drops as necessary. (Don't add too much water. Doing so can wash most of the lube away.)

5. Condoms, foams, suppositories, and other protective devices must be kept very close by. Remember, if you don't keep it handy, you won't take the time to use it.

6.   Incense can help create a wonderful atmosphere.

7.   Candles or a dimmable light source also help create a special, erotic atmosphere.

8.   A small flashlight can be useful in any number of situations. (If you're experimenting with bondage, make sure you also have a "blackout light" in place.)

A well-stocked nightstand contributes a lot toward helping your erotic play proceed smoothly. Rummaging through drawers, tromping off to the bathroom, or needing to make a quick trip to the kitchen can "break the spell" the two of you are creating. A small amount of planning ahead is well worth it.

Travelling   Supplies

For several years now, I have made it a point to always carry a few condoms, a pair of latex gloves, some small (grape-sized) packs of lubricant, and a couple of spermicidal suppositories in my jacket pocket. These inexpensive, readily portable supplies have enabled me to have several delightful (if somewhat unexpected) evenings that I otherwise would not have had. You never know when a wonderful opportunity may present itself. As the Boy Scouts say, "Be prepared."

What To Do If a Condom Fails

OK, guy, while having vaginal intercourse you look down and you see that the condom you were wearing has broken and you are now wearing a small latex ring around the base of your cock. Or maybe you look down and discover that the condom is gone. (You were thinking that this particular brand caused very little loss of sensation.) Perhaps you have already come. What do you do now?

STOP! Then, first of all, if she doesn't already know, you gotta tell her. Try not to sound too alarmed (she may regard what has happened as a big deal, or she may not), but let her know what happened.

OK, you told her. Now what? If you're worried about getting a sexually transmitted disease, go into the bathroom and wash your genitals several times with generous amounts of soap and water, then empty your bladder (and maybe drink fluids so you can "flush out" your urethra some more). One nurse who worked in a VD clinic told me that washing and urinating after sex would reduce a man's chances of getting gonorrhea by 50%. (She had no information about whether it reduced his chances of getting other diseases.) Another nurse, who also works in a VD clinic, told me that she spends a lot of her time treating "that unlucky 50%" of the men who had tried doing this and it didn't work.

This could be overkill, but after you shower, consider applying rubbing alcohol, hydrogen peroxide, or an antiseptic (Betadine, or a generic version of it, would be a good choice) as a final touch.

Again, this may be overkill, but I'll point out that it's possible to douche with a dilute Betadine-type solution. Also, as with men, rubbing alcohol, hydrogen peroxide, and antiseptic creams can be applied to the external genitals.

If you feel you need immediate advice, call your doctor or

clinic. If it's late at night (when these events tend to happen), consider calling a hospital emergency room. They won't consider such a call out of line.

In the morning, it's crucial (repeat, crucial) that you call your regular doctor, a local VD clinic, or family planning center for advice. They may want you to come in, either that day or within a day or two, for an examination. Among other things, if you're worried about getting pregnant they can arrange for you to get a "morning after" pill.

Perhaps the most important point of this essay is to point out, once again, that a condom by itself is just not adequate protection. Their failure rate is simply too high and, if you're not using anything else, you may not notice such a failure until it may be too late.

A Warning About SM

The following is closely based on material in "SM 101: A Realistic Introduction."

SM is the riskiest form of sex. In addition to all the dangers of regular "vanilla" sex (unwanted pregnancy, sexually transmitted disease, and so forth), considerable danger of physical injury and/or emotional trauma exists. Furthermore, the abuse potential of a situation in which one person is tied up and at the mercy of another is dreadful to contemplate.

SM is not so dangerous that it should be avoided altogether, but, like skydiving, mountain climbing, and auto racing, people must learn about its risks, and learn about how to deal with them, before getting involved. That is not happening anywhere near as much as it should. A recent article in the San Francisco *Chronicle* mentioned that 25% of all adults have at least experimented with bondage. Only a tiny percentage of such people receive adequate instruction.

Therefore, I have included some of the most basic SM safety teachings in this book. Such instruction is far, far from complete, but will help guide you away from the major danger areas. I have also included the addresses of a few of the larger and better known SM clubs around the country. I cannot overstress how important it is to get proper instruction, and learn the proper perspective and context for SM play, from qualified people. Your life may literally depend on it.

I need to add that the image of SM presented in most "adult" videos, books, and magazines has usually been terribly inaccurate and irresponsible. A very few are excellent. Most are dangerous, irresponsible crap.

I have written a very comprehensive book about SM's basic techniques and safety measures. It's carried at many leather stores and erotic boutiques across the country. If you have such a store near you, please see if they carry it. If they don't, send a self-addressed, stamped envelope to Greenery Press at 1447 Park Ave., Emeryville, CA 94608, for information about how to buy it directly. I, and probably the store, would also appreciate it if you would give them this address.

The fundamental teaching of SM is that it is consensual. Both parties agree to participate, and either party has the right to stop the activity for any reason whatsoever. Refusing to untie someone who has demanded to be untied is a serious crime. Remember, if it's not completely consensual, then it's rape.

The Tricks most relevant to SM in this book are #14, #50, #51, #52 and $53. Please give them another look.

The Dangers of Self-Bondage

Many people have bondage fantasies but no partner, so they bind themselves. The person interested in self-bondage faces a problem. They want to bind themselves so they can't escape, yet, obviously, eventually they will want release. What to do?

Self-bondage can be extremely dangerous. You know how risky it is to bind someone and then leave them alone. The self-bound person has this obvious problem.

I have heard of several deaths resulting from self-bondage that went wrong. Even more disturbing, many of these deaths involved highly experienced players who "knew what they were doing" yet died anyway. Most such fatalities involved gags, hoods, ropes around the neck, or some other devices that had the potential to restrict breathing.

Most self-bondage involves locking devices, especially around the wrists. The person works out some mechanism by which the keys again come within their grasp. If the device fails to work (and, sooner or later, it will fail) the self-bound person often has no other way to get free or summon help.

Also of critical importance, bondage not tight enough to quickly put the bound area to sleep may still be tight enough to do that gradually. The self-bound person's hands may go numb after an hour. If the keys fall within reach after that – trouble.

I experimented for a while with self-bondage, but gave it up after I had an incident that gave me a moment of nearly pure panic. I also found that, besides its dangers, self-bondage has other drawbacks.

First, you may rapidly discover that being in bondage without a "sweet tormentor" for company is *boring*. The vibrators, clamps, dildoes, and other gear that aroused you when you first put yourself in bondage may feel awful after your arousal fades – even if it doesn't malfunction or go out of adjustment. If, genius that you are, you set the situation up so you can't get loose for three hours, you may find that the last two hours and fifty minutes go on for a *very* long time.

You might try binding your breasts and genitals, but be very conservative about using anything that would restrict your breathing (gags, hoods, neck ropes), make you vulnerable to a fall (blindfolds) or restrict your limbs – especially your arms.

Self-bondage often seems like a good idea in fantasy, and offers plausible exploration, as long as *absolutely nothing* goes wrong. Remember that even a minor maladjustment of a piece of equipment can set the stage for hours of genuine suffering, and that a serious malfunction or unexpected development can cause you to die a slow, agonizing death. Many "experts" died exactly this way.

SM Clubs

The largest and best-known clubs in the United States are listed under "Sadomasochism" on p. 116. If you don't live near one, ask for a referral to a nearer club. Also, some of these clubs put out highly informative newsletters. You might therefore want to join anyway so you can receive them.

An Even Stronger Warning About Breath Control Play

(The following is an excerpt from my book "SM 101: A Realistic Introduction.")

Some people explore choking, suffocation, and other forms of "breath control." Why? Well, the first symptom of oxygen deprivation is often euphoria. Also, the idea of this degree of control can be compelling: one submissive woman gasped with wonder (and delight) when she considered that her master might "control the very air I breathe." Unfortunately, this area is the single most dangerous aspect of SM-related play.

After a great deal of investigation, consideration, and discussing this subject with people who have much more medical knowledge than I have, I have been unable to learn any way to make breath control play acceptably safe. Furthermore, the overwhelming majority of the SM-related fatalities I have heard of were related to restricting breathing.

The whole problem lies in determining how much is enough. It's similar to the old mechanic's joke: How tight should I tighten this bolt?... Tighten it up to a quarter-turn before it strips.

The goal of some forms of breath control play seems to be to render someone unconscious and then revive them. Unfortunately, the means used to render the person unconscious by interfering with the amount of oxygen to their brain also, and unknown by many people, affects their heart.

People usually appear to tolerate this well, but if there's a mishap – they die. Another serious problem is that every episode of unconsciousness seems to cause at least some permanent (repeat, *permanent*) brain damage.

There simply seems to be no safe way to play in this area. Police "judo chokes" designed to cause harmless unconsciousness have been banned by many departments because these holds caused deaths in many cases, sometimes hours after the choke was applied. "Experts" at breath-control-related erotic play have died because their "failsafe" devices failed. Even apparently safe practices such as ordering the submissive to hold their own breath or ordering them to hyperventilate can be far riskier than they seem to be.

"Auto-erotic asphyxiation" masturbation games cause hundreds of fatalities in otherwise healthy people each year. I was once involved in a resuscitation attempt on such a case during my ambulance days. I still remember my partner, myself, the cops, the fire department, and the hospital emergency room crew doing the best CPR we could on a young teenage boy while his mother yelled and screamed and prayed frantically to God to please, please, please not take her boy. (We got his heart going again, but he died the next day.)

I have researched this area a great deal, and I find no acceptably safe way to play with it. I have listened carefully to several "experts," and I've found alarming flaws in their reasoning and deficits in their knowledge. I have read literature associated with breath control play, and it also scares me. Stay away from this stuff.

Footnote: Because I hate to say that any erotic practice is so dangerous that it should never be done, I'm willing to listen further to advocates of breath control play. However, I've listened to some, and so far they have not only failed to impress me – they have appalled me.

You can write to me about how you think breath control play can be safely done if you want – but if you don't have a clear, detailed understanding of arterial blood gases, PVCs, the vagus nerve, asystole, syncope, acetylcholine, hypocarbia, tetany, ventricular fibrillation, and related subjects then you have absolutely no business telling anybody anything about breath control play other than to stay away from it.

Problems

Probably the most important advice I can give you regarding finding help for the problems listed below, and other problems, is to grab your phone book and start looking. Many communities have local resources. Check the first few pages and look over the table of contents. Look up these and related topics in both the white and yellow pages. Check your phone book for an index.

If this doesn't help much, go to your local library and look through the phone books of nearby communities, particularly those of nearby big cities.

Local newspapers and magazines, particular free or low-cost ones that come out on a weekly or less frequent basis, often carry valuable listings. Gay and lesbian papers can be particularly helpful. Look them over carefully.

The internet is an excellent source of information regarding sexuality-related problems. Look in the alt.recovery, alt.sex and alt.support hierarchies, and in any newsgroups that announce local events and groups in your community.

Abuse/Battering/Neglect

National Domestic Violence Hotline (800) 333-SAFE

National Child Abuse Hotline (800) 422-4453

Parents Anonymous (800) 421-0353

AIDS

National AIDS Hotline (800) 342-AIDS

National STD Hotline (800) 227-8922

Birth Control/Abortion

Check your local yellow pages under "Birth Control Information Centers." Note: Some anti-abortion agencies have been accused of being less than totally honest about that fact. If a given resource doesn't explicitly say that it offers abortions, please consider that its policies may be anti-abortion.

Censorship

American Civil Liberties Union
132 West 43rd St.
New York, New York 10036

National Coalition Against Censorship
132 West 43rd. Street
New York, New York 10036
(212) 944-9899

People for the American Way
2000 M. Street N.W., Suite 400
Washington, DC 20036
(202) 467-4999

Death During Sex

People, especially older men, die during sex far more often than is commonly believed. One of the reasons for this is that their partners are often too embarrassed to tell what was going on when the death occurred.

Studies have shown that the person in the community who faces the highest risk of sudden cardiac arrest is a man over the age of 50, and the person most likely to be with him when it happens is his wife. If your boyfriend or husband is over 50, I strongly recommend that you schedule such training.

Studies have also shown that the second highest risk group for a sudden cardiopulmonary emergency is, to simplify matters, anyone wearing diapers. If you help take care of young children, schedule a class that teaches infant and child CPR. (The technique differs considerably from that used on adults.)

You can look in the yellow pages under "First Aid Instruction" to find out where classes are offered. The American Red Cross, American Heart Association, some hospitals and emergency service agencies, and private firms all offer classes.

If you take a CPR class, try hard to get a good instructor. I suggest someone who has a minimum of one year of full-time experience in pre-hospital emergency care. A paramedic might be a good first choice. (Although people who are good at providing emergency care are not necessarily good at teaching others how to do that.)

Disabilities

The Lawrence Research Group, which publishes the Xandria Collection catalogs, puts out a specialized catalog of sex toys and advice for people with disabilities. This catalog also contains a page listing of sexuality resources for the disabled across the U.S. To receive this catalog, send $4 and a request for the Special Edition for Disabled People to:

Lawrence Research Group
P.O. Box 319005
San Francisco, CA 94131

Herpes

Herpes Resource Center (HRC)
P.O. Box 13827
Research Triangle Park, North Carolina 27709

These folks offer wonderful information for those coping with any aspect of herpes. Among other things, they sponsor a nationwide network of support groups. If somebody I cared about had herpes, I would make certain that they were fully informed about what these folks offer.

National STD Hotline (800) 227-8922

Incest

Incest Survivors Anonymous
P.O. Box 5613
Long Beach, CA 90805-0613
(310) 428-5599

Survivors of Incest Anonymous
P.O. Box 21817
Baltimore, Maryland 21222
(410) 433-2365

Both of these groups sponsor meetings all over the country. They will also help you start a group in your area if one does not already exist. Incest is one of the most under-reported forms of abuse in this country.

Old Age

Sex Over Forty Newsletter
PHE, Inc.
P.O. Box 1600
Chapel Hill, North Carolina 27515

As people age, their needs and their bodies change. This newsletter is one of the most informative and useful sources of information on the topic.

Rape

As soon as you safely can, call 911, a rape treatment center, or a similar resource. Check your phone book under Rape, Battering, and Sexual Abuse Aid. It's very important from a medical, emotional, and legal point of view to seek help as soon as possible after the assault.

Know that an attempted rape can be almost as damaging, and take as long to recover from, as a completed rape. If you can safely do so, have the authorities come to the scene so they can look for valuable evidence. Try not to shower, douche, brush your teeth, or change clothes until you've been examined.

If you need support or don't feel your case is being handled properly, by all means contact a rape crisis center for more help.

Sex Therapy

You don't necessarily need a formally trained sex therapist to help you cope with sexual problems. Many therapists with broader training do excellent work in this field.

That said, I want to mention that the organizations listed below help train and set policies for sex therapists. Someone representing themselves as a sex therapist would probably have extensive contact with at least one of them.

Sex therapy is not an exact science. In particular, such issues as the use of surrogates are highly controversial. You should understand that the organizations listed below are far from in total agreement on every issue. AASECT is considered the more conservative.

Society for the Scientific Study of Sex (SSSS)
P.O. Box 208
Mount Vernon, Iowa, 52314

American Association of Sex Educators, Counselors, and Therapists (AASECT)
435 Michigan Ave, Suite 1717
Chicago, Illinois 60611

Sex and Love Addiction

These are 12-step groups designed to help people achieve "sexual sobriety" by using the principles of Alcoholics Anonymous. They have chapters in many parts of the country. If one doesn't exist in your area, they will help you start one. (Don't be surprised if your initial outreach efforts draw more people than you expected.)

Sexaholics Anonymous
P.O. Box 300
Simi Valley, CA 93062

Sex and Love Addicts Anonymous
P.O. Box 119
New Town Branch
Boston MA 02258

Suicidal/Homicidal Feelings

Almost every local community has telephone crisis hotlines. Again, check your telephone book – particularly the first few pages.

Additional Resource Information

The organizations listed below offer referrals and a sympathetic ear. They most definitely do not, however, offer phone sex.

San Francisco Sex Information (415) 621-7300

Los Angeles Sex Information (213) 653-1123

Alternative Sexuality Resources

As with the "Problems" section, many resources can be found by carefully checking in your phone book and by visiting the library to check the phone books of nearby cities, particularly large ones. Also, many alternative sexuality clubs and other resources advertise in adult papers and other periodicals with an erotic slant.

The internet is also an excellent source of information regarding most forms of alternative sexuality. The majority of sexuality newsgroups fall under the alt.sex hierarchy, but some, typically more oriented toward philosophy, politics and discussion, can also be found in other hierarchies such as soc.*.

Important Notice: When writing to any of these organizations, it's wise to include a business-sized, self-addressed, stamped envelope.

Bisexuality

Bisexual Resource Center
> Robyn Ochs
> P.O. Box 639
> Cambridge, MA 02140
> (617) 338-9595

Body Size and Weight

National Organization to Advance Fat Acceptance (NAAFA)
P.O. Box 188630
Sacramento, CA 95818

A national support organization, with chapters in many cities, for fat people and their admirers.

Corsetry

For people who enjoy wearing corsets and people who enjoy people who enjoy wearing corsets.

B.R. Creations
P.O. Box 4201
Mountain View, CA 94040
Ask about their "Corset Newsletter."

Cross Dressing

ETVC
P.O. Box 426486
San Francisco, CA 94142

This is a respected educational and social organization for people exploring gender issues and those who care about them. It publishes a newsletter that contains many local resources, national resources, and information on other local groups around the country. Highly recommended.

International Foundation for Gender Education (I.F.G.E.)
P.O. Box 367
Wayland, MA 01778
(617) 894-8340

The organization publishes the "TV/TS Tapestry Journal," a 150+ page magazine containing articles, references and other resources. Sample copy $12.00. Again, highly recommended.

Expanded Families

PEP
Box 6306
Captain Cook, Hawaii 96704-6306

Nationwide organization promoting polyfidelity, group marriage, and expanded families.

Gay and Lesbian Resources

National Gay Yellow Pages ($10.00)
Box 292
Village Station
New York, New York 10014

Again, your local phone book should help you find resources in your area.

Infantilism

Diaper Pail Friends
38 Miller Avenue #127

Mill Valley, CA 94941

This is *not* about adults having sex with children. DPF is an organization for adults who enjoy dressing up and pretending to be babies.

Piercing, Scarification, and Other Body Modification

The following magazines contain wonderful introductory information and referrals for those who are into having more than their nose pierced. Warning: Piercing, scarification, branding, and other forms of body modification can cause injury or death if done improperly. Proper training and supervision is essential; never attempt these practices without it.

Body Play and Modern Primitives Quarterly
P.O. Box 421668
San Francisco, CA 94142-1668 Sample issue: $12.00.

Piercing Fans International Quarterly (PFIQ)
Gauntlet
8720 Santa Monica Blvd.
Los Angeles, CA 90069 Sample issue: $10.00

Penis Size, Shape, and so forth

Small, Etc.
P.O. Box 294
Bayside, New York 11361

NOCIRC (an anti-circumcision organization)
P.O. Box 2512
San Anselmo, CA 94960

Prostitute Support Groups
(Mailing addresses only. For sex workers only. No would-be customers need write!)

Coyote
2269 Chestnut Street # 452
San Francisco, CA 94123

Coyote – Los Angeles
1626 N. Wilcox Ave. # 580
Hollywood, CA 90028

Prostitutes of New York (PONY)
25 West 45th St., # 1401
New York, New York 10036

Hooking is Real Employment (HIRE)
P.O. Box 89386
Atlanta, GA 39359

Prostitutes Anonymous
11225 Magnolia Blvd. # 181
North Hollywood, CA 91601
For those who want to leave the sex industry or for help afterwards.

Swinging

This form of sexuality used to be called "wife-swapping."

North American Swing Club Association (NASCA)
P.O. Box 7128
Buena Park, CA 90622

Publishes "International Directory of Swing Clubs and Publications."

Sadomasochism

The following organizations are some of the largest. They are open to both men and women. They can provide referrals to those seeking all-male or all-female groups and to those seeking clubs closer to where they live. (Several new clubs form each year.)

Eulenspiegel Society (Believed to be the oldest SM club in the U.S.)
P.O. Box 2783 GCS
New York, New York 10163

Society of Janus
P.O. Box 426794
San Francisco, CA 94142-6794

Threshold
2554 Lincoln Blvd., # 381
Marina Del Rey, CA 90291

Tantra

Tantra, The Magazine
P.O. Box 79
Torreon, New Mexico 87061-9900

Tantra, and its cousins Quodoushka and Healing Tao, are spiritual pathways whose teachings and practices include sexuality. *Tantra, The Magazine* contains excellent listings and descriptions of classes, workshops, and other activities offered around the country.

Transgenderism

For those wishing to change their genders.

FTM (stands for Female-to-Male)
5337 College Ave. # 142
Oakland, CA 94618

San Francisco Gender Information
P.O. Box 423602
San Francisco, CA 94142

Gender Identity Center Newsletter
3715 West 32nd Ave.
Denver, CO 80211

TV/TS Tapestry Journal
Internatonal Foundation for Gender Education (IFGE)
P.O. Box 367
Wayland, MA 01778

Additional Alternative Sexuality Information

The organizations listed below offer referrals and a sympathetic ear. They most definitely do not, however, offer phone sex.

San Francisco Sex Information (415) 621-7300

Los Angeles Sex Information (213) 653-1123

Bibliography

"A New View of a Woman's Body" by The Federation of Feminist Women's
Health Centers
published by Feminist Press
8235 Santa Monica Blvd., Suite 201
West Hollywood, CA 90046

"The Complete Guide to Safer Sex"
Institute for Advanced Study of Human Sexuality
1525 Franklin Street
San Francisco, CA 94109

"For Play: 150 Sex Games for Couples"
by Walter Shelburne, Ph.D.
Waterfall Press
5337 College Avenue, #139
Oakland, CA 94618

Condom Educator's Guide, Version Two
by Daniel Bao and Beowulf Thorne
Condom Resource Center
P.O. Box 30564
Oakland, CA 94604
(510) 891-0455

"Sex: A User's Manual"
by The Diagram Group

"Anal Pleasure and Health: A Guide for Men and Women" (Second Edition)
by Jack Morin, Ph.D.
Yes Press
938 Howard Street
San Francisco, CA 94103

"The New Our Bodies, Ourselves: A Book By and For Women"
by The Boston Women's Health Book Collective
A Touchstone Book
published by Simon and Schuster

"The Good Vibrations Guide to Sex"
by Cathy Winks and Anne Semans
published by Cleis Press

"The Black Book"
edited by Bill Brent
P.O. Box 31155
San Francisco, CA 94131-0155
           A comprehensive national guide to sexuality clubs, stores,
publications and other resources.

Please Send Me Your Tricks
(but read this carefully first)

Do you do something that consistently drives your lovers wild? Would you like to share your Trick with the rest of us? Send it to me! I plan to publish more "Tricks" books. Maybe you can be a contributor.

Send me your Trick, preferably typed on one side of a standard sheet of paper. Please date the paper and include illustrations as necessary. If I use your Trick, I'll send you a free copy of the book it appears in and, if you wish, put your name on the "thank you" list in that book. Because of "independent discovery" it's impossible for me to credit a particular person with a particular Trick. (I repeatedly encountered independent discovery while researching this book.)

Also, again because of independent discovery, I'll undoubtedly receive letters from different people describing essentially the same Trick, and I can only afford to reward the first person who clearly describes the Trick in question. So, again, please date your letter. (Actually, I'll probably send a book to the first three or so people who send in a given Trick.)

You can increase your chances of inclusion by sending more than one Trick. One per page, please. Please don't send more than ten Tricks a year. I wouldn't have time to properly consider them.

Let me know what type of credit you want on the "thank you" list. You may choose between anonymous, first name only, initials only, your nickname, or your full legal name. If you wish, I can also include your city. If you sign your Trick with your full name, be honest about your identity and include your address and phone number. Signing another person's name to a letter is a crime, and I will verify all full names before publishing them.

Please send your Trick only by regular first class mail. Spare me from certified letters, registered letters, and so forth. If you don't feel you can trust me, please don't send me your Trick. Also, please don't put a copyright notice on it. A unique usage of words can be copyrighted, but not what such words describe. (This is what allows dozens of reporters to each write a story about the same incident.) Also, I'd almost undoubtedly need to re-write your words while preserving the essence of your Trick.

Please don't send anything "too far out" or dangerous. Letters dealing with children or animals will be immediately turned over to the police.

Please don't send anything regarding political issues, economic concerns, social problems, and so forth. Again, those matters deserve books of their own. (However, if you know of a widely available resource that can help someone with a personal problem closely related to sexuality, I would love to share that information with my readers.)

I was utterly unprepared for the volume of mail that resulted from the publication of my other books. This will add to my load, and I'm already chronically behind in answering that. I therefore can't promise you an individual reply. Including a self-addressed, stamped envelope will help somewhat, but please don't get your hopes up too far. Also, I won't know until just before publication whether or not your Trick was included, so please don't write and ask. You'll know very shortly after I know.

I apologize if the above seems negative and restrictive, but it reflects learning from experience. If you would be happy with a book and being on the "thank you" list, but wouldn't be too disappointed if your Trick didn't make it, then I would genuinely love to hear from you. This world can use a little more pleasure. I hope you help contribute to that.

Send your Tricks to: Jay Wiseman, c/o Greenery Press, 1447 Park Ave., Emeryville, CA 94608.

SEX TOY TRICKS

SEX TOY TRICKS

Table of Contents

Warning and Disclaimer 129

Why Am I Writing This Book? 131

Criteria 134

The Limits Of Tricks 136

Intoxicants 138

Sex and the Internet 139

Where To Buy Sex Toys 140

A Tour of an Erotic Boutique 145

A Few Don'ts Regarding Tricks 155

TRICKS **157**

Latex Allergy 207

How to Clean Toys After Use 210

What to Do If You "Lose" Something In the Rectum 213

The Five "Shuns" of Anal Play 216

Twenty SM Safety Tricks 219

Problems 231

Alternative Sexuality Resources 237

Please Send Me Your Tricks 245

Acknowledgements
(The "Thank You" List)

It's been a distinct privilege to talk with the various people listed below. I feel very honored that they would judge me trustworthy enough to share such very personal experiences and knowledge. I hope I have done justice to what they shared. My grateful thanks to all.

Ann Marie
Annye and Christophe
Anonymous
Cecilia Tan
Charles Moser
China
Dell Williams
Don't tell them where you got that
Dossie Easton
Francesca Guido
Glenna
Helen Wolfe
Jaymes Easton
Jennifer Thompson
Joan Levine
John Warren
Karen Kummerfeldt
Karen Mendelsohn
Kim Airs
Leona Joy
Libby Donahue
Lynn Craig
Maggi Rubenstein
Maryann
Merrill Seldes
Mic Bergen
Moriah St. Cyr
Ms. Margo
Nightlace
Oberon and Morning Glory Zell
Tedde Rinker-Davis
Trish
Verdant
Wally Daniels
Wilhelmina Moosepunch

Additional Thanks

Staff members of the following stores also graciously contributed material. If you call, please mention this book.

Note: The stores listed below are something of a mixed lot. Most are retail, walk-in stores, but some are mail-order-only operations. Some offer merchandise and books, and some only offer books. Some offer classes and workshops.

Blowfish San Francisco, CA (415) 864-0880
Camouflage Santa Cruz, CA (408) 423-7613
Circlet Press P.O. Box 15143 Boston, MA
Come Again New York, NY (212) 308-9394
Diversified Services Boston, MA (617) 787-7426
Good Vibrations San Francisco, CA (415) 974-8989
Grand Opening Boston, MA (617) 731-2626
Love Season Lynnewood, WA (206) 775-4502
Passion Flower Oakland, CA (510) 601-7750
Pleasure Chest Philadelphia, PA (215) 561-7480
QSM San Francisco, CA (415) 550-7776
Taboo Tabou Chicago, IL (312) 548-2266
The Noose New York, NY (212) 807-1789
Toys In Babeland Seattle, WA (206) 328-2914
Xandria Brisbane, CA (800) 242-2823

If you'd like for your store to be listed in future printings, feel free to contact us with some Tricks of your own.

Finally, once again, my deepest thanks to Janet. Thank you for five wonderful, deeply loving, years together – with (please, God) more to come! Thank you for being one of the most brilliant, insightful, creative, and sex-positive women that ever existed. Thank you for your many contributions to helping make this book a reality. Finally, and a bit humbly, thank you for your world-class patience with me during the final stages of this book's creation. I love you absolutely, unconditionally, and with all my heart, just the way you are.

April 28, 1995 San Francisco, CA.

Warning and Disclaimer

Being sexual with the right person, in the right way, at the right time, in the right location, and for the right reasons can be an incredibly positive experience for everyone involved. If any of the above is not right, however, then problems can emerge.

Erotic energy is one of the most powerful forces in our world. Respect and pay attention to that power and you can experience bliss. Disrespect or ignore that power and you might not live to regret it.

The primary purpose of "Sex Toy Tricks" is to provide information and advice that will help make good sex between informed, consenting adults a little bit better. It also provides basic information to help people understand their situations, make them aware of possible alternatives, cope with problems, and find helpful resources.

Please do not think of this book as any kind of medical, legal, psychological, or other professional advice. It most certainly is not intended as a substitute for proper sex therapy. Most of its core information, particularly the "Tricks" themselves, was discovered on my own, taught to me by lovers I have had, shared with me by friends during highly informal conversations (many has been the time since the first "Tricks" book was published that someone has come up to me and said "I've got a Trick for you"), or sent to me either in the mail or over the internet. Please keep that in mind when considering this book's contents.

Almost without question, there are at least a few factual errors in this book, and probably a few typographical errors as well. Also, it's very common, in this and many other fields, that information believed to be accurate at the time of publication is later revealed to be inaccurate – sometimes only slightly so, sometimes very much so. If you have even the slightest question about the accuracy or safety of anything in here, please check with independent sources. If their recommendations differ from mine, please let me know. By the way, please remember that not all professional advice is equally complete, accurate, up to date, and unbiased. By all means get an independent "second opinion" (and maybe even a "third opinion") if you feel even the slightest need for it.

Feedback Please!

If you think you have found a factual error, typographical error, or other inaccuracy or omission in this book, please let me know so that this can be corrected in future printings.

No one associated with writing, editing, printing, distributing, or selling this book, or in any other way associated with it, is in any way liable for any damages that result from acting on the information herein. While I have most certainly not put anything in here that I consider likely to be harmful, understand clearly that you act on the information in this book entirely at your own risk.

Why Am I Writing This Book?

The Scope of This Book

Well, folks, the saga of the "Tricks" books continues to grow. As some of you know, I had a "Tricks" article appear in the December, 1994 issue of <u>Playboy</u> (the one with Bo Derek's face on the cover). People continue to send me Tricks in the mail, or over the internet (I'm oldrope@aol.com), or to tell me about them in person. I must confess that I never expected such an overwhelming reaction.

That I should be writing this particular book is also more than slightly surprising to me. (Was it John Lennon who said "Life is what happens while you're making other plans?") In 1994, it dawned on me that I had a logical gap in my line of sexuality books. I had my "Tricks" books, which involved mainly the bodies of the people involved (and a few household items), and I had "SM 101: A Realistic Introduction" to tell people the basics of how to use SM equipment, but I didn't have a book that dealt with ordinary sex toys. Thus was born the idea for this book.

This book deals with how to use items that were manufactured and purchased specifically for relatively "vanilla" sexual activity. It will not deal extensively with SM-type activities and/or equipment – although it will cover some basic SM safety info.

Assumptions

In presenting the material in this book, I am making the following assumptions about your situation. If any of these assumptions are not true in your case, please modify your behavior accordingly.

I'm assuming:

1.   That both of you are willing (and, hopefully, eager) to have sex with each other. Consent is absolutely essential.

2.   That being sexual with each other will not violate any agreements you have made with others about your sexual behavior.

3.   That both of you reasonably understand what you are doing. Having sex with someone too young, senile, feeble-minded, intoxicated, unconscious, or otherwise unable to understand and consent to what is happening may get you charged with rape, even if no force was used. If they're too drunk to drive, they're probably too drunk to have sex.

4.   That both of you have reached the age of consent in your state (and that you live in the United States). I believe the age of consent is as low as twelve in a few states and as high as eighteen in many others. An act that is perfectly legal on one side of a state line may cost you a lengthy prison sentence if done on the other side of it. Make sure you know the age of consent in your state.

Your local library should have a copy of your state's criminal code in its reference section. Reading its sections on rape, incest, indecent exposure, lewd and lascivious behavior, assault, contributing to the deliquency of a minor, and related sections may be very instructive. Asking a local attorney or police officer (that you already know well) can also help, but remember that opinions, knowledge, and objectivity can vary widely, even among such "experts." Try to get information from more than one source.

(By the way, sex between blood relatives may be illegal no matter what the age of those involved. If you cannot legally marry a particular person, it may also be illegal for you to have sex with each other. This could be true even if both of you are over 18 and both fully consent.)

5.   That the acts I'm describing are legal in your state. Although the laws are rarely enforced, oral sex, anal intercourse, and other practices are still a crime in some states, even if done by consenting adults in private. (Possession of some sorts of sex toys is against the law in some areas.) Find out your state's laws and, where appropriate, work to change them. This whole area is badly in need of legislative reform.

6.   That no risk of passing on a sexually transmitted disease exists. These days, that's a *big* assumption. If such a risk does exist, please modify what you do. If you have herpes or if you have tested positive for the HIV virus and have sex with someone without first telling them about that, you could be arrested. If your partner becomes infected, you could also be sued. If you have any questions, one information source is the National Sexually Transmitted Disease Hotline at (800) 227-8922.

Criteria

For inclusion in this book, a Trick usually had to meet the following criteria:

1. It had to be something that could be done pretty much on impulse in the here and now. Nothing too elaborate.

2. It had to involve equipment purchased specifically for the purpose of erotic enjoyment – not ordinary household goods (that's "Supermarket Tricks"), but items intended only for sexual use.

3. It had to be safe. I included nothing I thought likely to endanger people.

4. It had to pertain directly to sex or to a very closely related matter.

5. It had to have a successful track record. I looked for Tricks that had consistently made more than one lover gasp, sigh, and moan.

6. It had to appeal to a wide, mainstream audience. The Trick couldn't be too far out or kinky. (Again, that's another book.) Most of the Tricks therefore involve masturbation, fellatio, cunnilingus, vaginal penetration, and anal penetration.

Selection, Balance, and Orientation

The Tricks in this book are largely a reflection of the material I received. I interviewed dozens of sex toy fans, male and female, gay, straight, and bisexual, to come up with the Tricks you see here.

I've tried to present as many Tricks as possible in a "gender neutral" manner. In most cases, it doesn't matter whether the people involved are straight or gay.

Please remember that I publish a series of "Tricks" books. If you feel a certain category is under-represented, by all means send in material to balance things out.

I deliberately included many masturbation Tricks in this book as my own way of encouraging safer sex.

I decided to, for the most part, leave out material regarding SM, bisexuality, swinging, tantra, multiple-partner sex, and so forth. Those are specialized areas, and their practices and customs are far too extensive to describe properly in this book. I did include contact information if you're interested in exploring them further. You may also find useful information in some of my other books (listed on the last page).

The Limits Of Tricks

You know, and I know, that lovemaking should not be reduced to Tricks. Tricks are to erotic play what spices are to food. A few carefully chosen ones make the experience more intense and pleasurable. Too many spoil things.

It's entirely possible to have a wonderful and completely satisfying sex life without knowing the Tricks in this book, or any others. Good sex is based on caring about your partner's well-being, really wanting to have sex with them (and, of course them really wanting to have sex with you), and observing the responsibilities that go along with that. Still, adding a carefully chosen spice now and then helps things along.

Key Point: Your underlying feelings towards the other person, and theirs toward you, greatly affect whether or not a Trick will improve your erotic play. As one lady told me, "If I really like him, then he almost can't do anything wrong. If I really don't like him, then he can't even breathe right."

When a Trick Bombs

Each person has their own unique physical and emotional pattern of erotic responsiveness. Every now and then a Trick that always worked well before may utterly turn off a new partner. The key phrase for handling this situation is "show compassion for everyone involved, including yourself."

If what you did *really* turned your partner off, try not to take it personally. (You wouldn't be human if you didn't take it somewhat personally, but don't buy into that too deeply.) Remember, each person has their own pattern, and you can never completely know that pattern. Give them a brief apology, if that seems appropriate, then move on to something else. Little will be gained by debating the point, particularly right then. Save discussions for later.

On the other hand, if your partner starts to do something that really doesn't work for you, diplomatically let them know that as soon as you can. Being "polite" in this situation will only allow your displeasure to build to uncontrollable levels. Speak up (politely, please) as soon as possible. Remember, this is almost undoubtedly not willful misconduct on their part. They are probably doing it in an attempt, however misguided, to arouse you. Speak up – but give them the benefit of the doubt, especially if this partner is relatively new.

Find Their Envelope

Each person has their own erotic response pattern, something I've come to think of as their "envelope." One of your main tasks as a good lover is to find your partner's envelope. Something that is wildly erotic for one person can be grossly unpleasant, and even traumatic, for another.

The envelope varies widely from person to person. It also varies over time with the same person. Find their envelope before you try too many Tricks, and remember that the location and content of that envelope change over time.

Intoxicants

Provided you don't have a substance abuse problem, light use of intoxicants can do a lot to enhance your mood. They can relax tense muscles, take your mind off the worries of the day, and generally calm you down and bring you into the here and now.

I prefer wine. Beer tends to fill up my bladder too quickly (and too often). Harder liquors take me more out of it than I like. I quit using recreational drugs of any kind many years ago.

More than light intoxicant use is asking for trouble. Your judgment becomes dangerously cloudy. Your coordination suffers. You may become too out of it to be sexual at all.

AIDS prevention experts are campaigning against combining sex and intoxicants. They have found that many unsafe sex acts occur when, and – more importantly – only when, the people involved are intoxicated. They compare driving under the influence (D.U.I.) with having sex under the influence (S.U.I.) in terms of danger.

Remember that getting someone too drunk or stoned to understand what is happening and then having sex with them is rape.

If someone is so drunk or stoned that it would be a crime for them to drive, then it would also probably be a crime to have sex with them.

Sex and the Internet

In the last few years, the international computer network known as the Internet has skyrocketed in usage – particularly its sexuality-related areas.

Some places on the Internet, devoted to the discussion of specific subjects, are called newsgroups. There, people can read and place messages related to the topic. Several thousand newsgroups exist and about 100 new ones appear each month. In addition, thousands of pages on the World Wide Web are devoted to sexuality issues – search engines such as Yahoo can help you find them. If you're interested in aviation, bicycling, stamp collecting, MTV, or virtually any other subject, you can find an international network of kindred spirits on the net.

More than a dozen newsgroups are devoted to various aspects of sexuality. Most are called "alt" (for alternative) groups. Some of the best-known are:

soc.sexuality.general
soc.subculture.bondage-bdsm
soc.subculture.bondage-bdsm.femdom
alt.polyamory
alt.sexual.abuse.recovery

In addition, at least two newsgroups exist for the sole purpose of marketing sex-related goods. Check out alt.sex. marketplace and alt.sex.erotica.marketplace (the busier of the two) for more information. I can be reached as wisemanjay@aol.com on the net.

Where To Buy Sex Toys

I've got to write this chapter carefully, because I can visualize all my vendors jumping up and down shouting "From me! From me!" I do suggest that you give your business to a local resource if possible.

There are three major sources of toys: walk-in retail stores, mail-order vendors, and pleasure parties. Let's look at each.

How to Find Walk-in Sex Toy Vendors in Your Local Community

Open your yellow pages to "Lingerie Dealers, Retail" and begin your search there. Then turn to "Bookstores," "Leather," and "Videos." In addition to traditional adult bookstores, we now have a growing number of "sex-positive" erotic boutiques and leather stores. If you can, visit several different stores before making purchases. (Most are open on weekends, so spending the day touring them with your partner can make for a wonderful "erotic holiday.")

Different stores cater to different clienteles. Most traditional adult bookstores are aimed at heterosexual men. Some stores attract a mostly gay male clientele. Some are aimed primarily at women. You may be treated in subtly (or not so subtly!) different ways at different stores. Try to give your business to a store in which you feel comfortable.

A Caution for Straight Men

One caution that I'll give to my straight male readers: you might think it would be a great idea to try to hang out in the women-oriented stores trying to meet partners. I can just hear some of you thinking, "Hey, *lots* of babes go into places like that, and they're already horny. This will be almost too easy."

The truth is that a woman, especially if she is by herself, may be hyper-nervous about being in such a store. Any pick-up attempts, no matter how "innocent and friendly," may send her bolting for the door, perhaps never to return – and that's tragic. Such behavior has a *very* good chance of getting you kicked out, and perhaps permanently banned. Trying to pick up women in an erotic boutique is just not a good idea. Don't do it. (The clerks don't let other women hit on their female customers, either.)

Guys, if you want to go to a woman-oriented erotic boutique to buy toys, books, and so forth, by all means go. They'd love your business. Just understand that these places have had to deal with a lot of male jerks, so they may act slightly wary towards you. When I go into such a store, I always keep my distance from the women customers, and I wouldn't dream of speaking to one of them unless she spoke to me first.

It's fine to ask the female clerks questions about the literature or equipment, and they should be happy to make recommendations. Just don't get too explicit. They're not getting paid to "talk sexy" with you – and they have to deal with such nonsense entirely too often.

As a subpoint, it's fine to call on the phone and ask about store hours, location, and so forth. Just keep your conversation businesslike and brief. Asking her to "describe every item in the store and tell me how to use it" will likely get you little except a dial tone (or a curt and businesslike suggestion that you buy and read this very book).

A Few Suggestions for the Nervous Woman

Many women report major, positive changes in their lives, and not just their sex lives, after reading literature or using equipment they bought in an erotic boutique. Indeed, sometimes just going into one can be a revealing, educational experience. More and more erotic boutiques go out of their way to make female customers comfortable. Please don't let your fears become so strong that you never go.

Here are a few hints about how to gather your courage.

1.   **Going in is not really all that risky.**

You are not likely to be approached by horny, crude male (or female) customers. The staff, like the staff of any store, would probably be quite happy if you bought something. They have no reason to make you feel uncomfortable, and many reasons to make you feel comfortable. It's very common to have a "hey, that was fun!" feeling after a first visit.

2.   **Go with friends, particularly female friends.**

There is courage in numbers. You can lend each other emotional support, and the visit can become a delicious subject for later conversations. Remember, you don't have to buy something with all of your friends looking on; you can come back later by yourself. Also, many stores sell by mail order, so you can look over the merchandise and quietly snag a mail-order catalog, or call the store later and ask them to send you one.

3.   **Go with one close friend or your primary partner.**

You almost undoubtedly won't need someone to "protect" you during your visit to an erotic boutique, but going with someone can provide some reassurance. Just make sure it's someone with whom you feel comfortable talking about the store's merchandise.

4.   **Go at a time when the store is not very busy.**

Erotic boutiques tend to be busier on weekends than during the week. During the week, they are often busier in the late afternoon and early evening, when people get off work, than earlier during the day. They are also busier than usual before Christmas and Valentine's Day.

5. **Go to a store in another town.**

While I still feel it's best to buy locally if you can, sometimes it's prudent to wait until you're in another city, where nobody is likely to know you – especially if you're well known in your local community. (When, oh when, will we begin to regard sexuality as just another part of life? We don't have these concerns regarding visits to a grocery or hardware store.) Many people take advantage of a trip to cities like New York or San Francisco to "sneak in" a visit to an erotic boutique.

6. **Above all else, go.**

Whatever strategy you adopt, an actual visit to an erotic boutique can be a moving experience that can teach you a lot about yourself, sexuality, and other aspects of life. If you're interested in a visit, please don't let your fears cheat you.

Mail-Order Businesses

Several companies do a first-rate job of providing information and equipment by mail order. They're not hard to find. (After all, *they're* trying to find *you*.) Many run ads in periodicals that deal with sexuality, relationships, and/or health issues. Magazines aimed specifically at a male or at a female audience often contain such ads, usually toward the back. Mail-order companies also advertise on the internet's alt.sex.marketplace and alt.sex.erotica.marketplace newsgroups, as well as on the World Wide Web.

These companies may want a few dollars, which they will usually credit towards your first order, in exchange for their catalogs. These catalogs often contain a lot of information, and allow you to comparison shop. I suggest you acquire at least three.

Pleasure Parties

These events, usually all-female but occasionally for couples, in many ways resemble "Tupperware parties" except that the goods being sold probably won't end up in your refrigerator or pantry. Typically, a woman hosts such a party in her home and invites several female friends. The (female) sales rep displays the various items and provides information on their use. Orders for goods are often taken in private and may be fullfilled either at the event or by later delivery. These events are often both highly educational and a great deal of fun. To learn more, check your phone book under "Party Planning."

In summary, you have several effective options for buying sex toys. Do some comparing and find the one that feels most comfortable to you.

A Tour of an Erotic Boutique

Let's take a look around a "typical" erotic boutique. These have come into being since the sexual revolution of the late Sixties and early Seventies. Most are owned/managed/staffed by women, and have a distinctly woman-oriented style. These stores almost always welcome men provided the guys keep in mind what the female staff and customers are there for – and *not* there for.

The stores contain a wide variety of merchandise. Indeed, a few are so jammed that it can be a bit difficult to move around in them. They will usually stock a variety of books (including such timeless classics as "Tricks," "SM 101," and "The Sexually Dominant Woman") and a number of sexuality-related magazines.

Many also carry videos, lingerie, jewelry (keep your eyes open for the "clit clip" and the "tit-a-lizer"), erotic board games, novelty items, lubricants, SM gear, and, of course, a wide variety of condoms, gloves, and other safer sex supplies.

And then there are the toys, all those marvelous toys – and so many different types of them! Let's look at the major categories and cover some of the basic points.

Vibrators

Some people get nervous about the idea of using a vibrator or other sex toy. Please trust me when I say that they're not addictive and that they'll never replace a cuddly partner. (They can be a wonderful supplement, however, for both of you.) There are two general categories of vibrators – plug-in and battery-powered – and many different subtypes of each.

The only vibrator problem reported with any noticeable frequency is that sometimes prolonged exposure to the stronger sensations produced by some vibrators can make the stimulated area temporarily less sensitive to more subtle forms of stimulation, or even to the vibration itself. This is called "numbing out" and goes away within half an hour or so. With vibrators, as with other sex toys, part of your learning and exploration involve discovering what's "too little," what's "too much," and what's "just right" (ahhhhhhh) for you. Relax, explore, and enjoy.

Plug-In Vibrators

Plug-in vibrators, as a rule, provide stronger, more spread-out vibrations than battery-operated vibrators provide. However, their electrical motors also give off considerably more heat. (If you run an plug-in vibrator long enough, it can become too hot to touch to bare skin. Prolonged usage can also damage the motor. Be sure to read, and save, the directions.) Most such vibrators come with two different speed settings. Most also come with a cord at least six feet long, but you'll probably find it a good idea to purchase an extension cord. (It's also possible to buy an adapter called the Humdinger 2 that goes between the plug and the wall socket and turns the vibrator's steady, constant buzz into a variable-speed pulsation.)

Plug-in vibrators come in two general subcategories: wand-type and coil-type. Both types have many loyal fans.

Wand-Type Plug-In Vibrators. Most wand-type vibrators have a vibrating head that attaches by a narrow, flexible neck to a long, cylindrical handle. (There's even a two-headed version!) Wand-type vibrators come very highly recommended. While I hesitate to make specific recommendations, the Hitachi Magic Wand is definitely worth checking out. (I recently bought one to give as a present.) It's also possible to buy attachments, such as a g-spot stimulator, to fit over the wand's head.

A wand-type rechargeable vibrator is on the market and well regarded. Users state that its vibrations are almost as strong as those from a regular wand, and they like its cordlessness. A single charge usually lasts forty minutes or so.

Coil-Type Plug-In Vibrators. Most coil-type vibrators are smaller than the wand-types, and have a handle on one end – kind of like a hairbrush. A small post protrudes from the bottom of the main section, and attachments go there. Coil-type vibrators usually have a more focused vibration and typically cost slightly less than wand-type vibrators. As a rule, coil-types tend to be quieter than wand-types. The store should let you turn on a few different types to check this. Coil-types also come with a wide variety of attachments. (An adapter is available to also make these attachments usable on wand-type vibrators.) One of my past lovers made a point of gleefully trying out every single attachment that came with my coil-type vibrator.

A unique sub-variety of coil-type vibrator is the "Swedish Massager," worn on the back of the hand to allow skin-to-skin contact.

When cleaning both wand and coil types of vibrators, be sure cleaning fluid doesn't get into the motor section. Wipe the exterior with a moistened cloth and allow to dry. The attachments (but not the vibrators themselves!) are "dunkable" and can even be run through the dishwasher.

One caution: Some wand-type vibrators (which are usually sold in more conventional stores) have the capacity to give off "deep heat" if you throw a specific switch. I have heard reports of severe burns from using this feature during genital play. Obviously, this is not a recommended practice.

Battery-Operated Vibrators

Many, many different varieties of battery-operated vibrators exist. The "standard" seven-inch by one-inch plastic vibrator is probably the most widely used sex toy in the world.

Battery-operated vibrators are relatively inexpensive, highly portable, and widely available. Their vibration tends to be less strong than that of a plug-in vibrator. They range from thumb-sized to more than a foot long. Battery-operated vibrators come in both single-speed and multiple speed versions. They are made of plastic, soft vinyl, latex, and other materials. Those made from a special soft synthetic compound are called "jellies."

Battery-operated vibrators come in many, many different sizes and shapes. The major types include:

– Standard, penis-shaped vibrators ranging in length from four inches to nearly a foot long and from less than one inch to more than two inches in diameter.

– Vibrators flared at the base with small bumps or beads contained within the vibrator to give additional stimulation to the outer portion of the vaginal canal (where most of her nerves are).

– Mostly straight vibrators that curve at the end to use for G-spot stimulation.

– "Butterfly" vibrators that lie over the woman's vulva and attach to her body by two straps.

– "Over and Under" vibrators that consist of a vibrator for internal stimulation and a separate clitoral stimulator on top, with a separate, variable speed control for each function. (These also have something of a cult following.)

- There is one particular type of battery-operated vibrator that I suggest you make a point of checking out. It goes by various names including the "bullet" and the "pearl." It's a very small, relatively inexpensive, cylinder-shaped vibrator – only two inches long and less than an inch in diameter – with a cord leading to its battery pack. This small size allows it to get into a number of places that a larger vibrator just can't go. (To use it for anal insertion, see Trick 116.) A number of stores recommend this particular model as a "first vibrator."

Ben Wa Balls

These are two balls inserted into the vagina. The smaller ones are all metal and not joined together. The larger ones (Duotone) contain a metal ball within a plastic ball, with the movement of the small ball inside the larger creating the sensations, and are joined by a loop of string. Like the bullet, you should take precautions if you're using ben wa balls for anal insertion.

Many women report that the sensation of ben wa balls alone is too subtle for them. However, those who love them really do love them – and many of those who don't are converted by using them in concert with other sex toys and activities. (For example, some women can wear the small metal ones during intercourse.)

Cock Rings

The arteries that carry blood into the penis are located deep within it and the veins that carry blood out of the penis are located closer to the surface. By applying a constricting band – usually around both the penis and the scrotum – an erection can often be made firmer and more long-lasting; how much so varies from man to man. This constricting band is commonly known as a cock ring.

Cock rings come in many different forms. They are made of leather, latex, steel, and other materials. Some encircle both the penis and scrotum, some encircle only the penis. Some come with stimulators for her vaginal/clitoral area. Some also wrap around the top of the scrotum and/or between the testicles (reminding me of that bra commercial advising how it "lifts and separates"). Some come with attachment points for bondage games. Some even come with a small vibrator attached.

For starters, I suggest that you buy a simple leather cock ring. They're inexpensive, highly adjustable, can be worn just around the scrotum, just around the penis, or around both penis and scrotum. Experiment to find the desired degree of tightness. A "too tight" cock ring can make orgasm painful, and even divert some to the semen up into the bladder. A "too loose" cock ring is of little value or interest. A "just right" cock ring is delightful for all concerned.

Dildoes

My dictionary defines a dildo as an artificial penis, although many folks uncomfortable with that implication prefer to define it as a device for penetrative sex. A dildo can be used for vaginal intercourse, anal intercourse, or fellatio play. Like vibrators, dildoes come in many different sizes, colors, and configurations. There are even double-headed models.

Dildoes are made of many different materials, including latex, rubber, "jelly," vinyl, leather, and silicone. Those flared at the base can be worn in a harness. (Adapters can be purchased that allow other dildoes to also be used this way.)

Many, many people, both men and women, love to be penetrated by a woman who is wearing a strap-on dildo. With the right partner and under the right circumstances, this can be an incredibly powerful experience for both people. Several different brands of harnesses are on the market, in a wide variety of configurations, materials, colors, and prices.

Silicone dildoes generally come highly recommended. They have distinctly life-like heft and flexibility, and they warm to body temperature quite nicely. However, they are noticeably more expensive than most other dildoes. Also, while they are reasonably sturdy, once a rip or tear starts in a silicone dildo there is usually little that can be done to save it. (Keep it away from various sharp points and abrasive surfaces – including the claws and teeth of family pets!) Some users report that silicone gets "floppy" after two or three years. I'm not sure

I'd recommend a silicone dildo as a first purchase, but once you decide that you're "into" dildo play they're definitely worth a serious look. In particular, a double headed dildo called the "Animus Activator" (also sometimes called the boomerang) is worth a close look.

Butt Plugs

The anus and rectum are very erotic areas for many people. Some lucky folks can reach orgasm from anal stimulation alone. However, the rectum is a delicate area, and care must be taken not to damage it. Also, unlike the vagina, the rectum is not a closed-end system. Objects can and do get lost up into the rectum. (That complication is dealt with in a separate section of this book.) As a basic safety matter, toys intended for anal play should have some sort of device designed to prevent their being "inhaled" by the rectum. For most toys, this is a broad flare at their base.

Like vibrators and dildoes, butt plugs come in a variety of colors, sizes, and materials. It's important that a butt plug have a smooth surface, with no sharp seams or "rough spots." Trust me, such places will quickly become unpleasantly evident.

Butt plugs are slightly different than dildoes, and usually used differently. Plugs typically have a bulge slightly above the flared end, designed to keep the wearer from involuntarily pushing out the plug. Unlike dildoes, which are frequently thrust in and out in a manner similar to intercourse, butt plugs are usually inserted and left in place.

Anal beads are a form of "butt plug" worth special attention. They are a series of beads (various sizes are available) strung along a string. The beads are inserted one at a time into the rectum. Pulling them out, slowly or quickly according to taste, can create arousal or boost orgasm. Anal beads can be used during both self-play and partner play. One caution: Unfortunately, they often have a rough "seam" on them that could cause discomfort and even injury if removed too quickly. Be sure to inspect each bead and carefully file down any rough seams before you insert them.

SM Gear

Many stores now carry "formal" items of SM gear such as whips, restraints, and clamps. As you look these items over, please keep in mind that SM can potentially be extremely risky to your physical health, your emotional health, and the health of your relationship with your partner. To do SM safely, you'll need to get some "formal" training.

There are many excellent beginners' books on the market. Look for my own "SM 101: A Realistic Introduction." Also look for "The Sexually Dominant Woman: A Workbook for Nervous Beginners" by Lady Green, "The Loving Dominant" by John Warren, "Learning the Ropes" by Race Bannon, "Sensuous Magic" by Pat Califia, and "Screw the Roses, Send Me the Thorns," by Philip Miller and Molly Devon.

Most large cities now have clubs that offer lectures on how to engage in SM with adequate safety and consensuality. Feel free to ask the clerk about such clubs in your area. There are also several excellent discussion groups regarding this topic on the Internet, and informational sites on the World Wide Web.

SM is not just another form of sexuality. It has incredible potential, but it also has incredible risks. Both these facts require that you approach it in much the same way that you would approach something like scuba diving or mountain climbing. There is a lot to learn, and you need to go slowly at first.

Lubricants, Gels, Creams, and Lotions

Lubricants are almost more of a necessity than an accessory. They're a must for anal play, and often very useful for vaginal play. Older women often welcome some supplemental vaginal lubrication.

Advisory: When a vibrator is touched to skin, particularly one of the stronger vibrators, the rapid back-and-forth motion can sometimes actually abrade the area. "Vibrator burn" can be a real nuisance. Consider applying a layer of lubricant beforehand, particularly if you're using a strong vibrator on a sensitive body area. (Such lubrication can also make the sensation considerably more pleasant, even in the absence of problems.)

Different lubricants are meant for different purposes. Lubricants basically come in two general types: water-based and oil-based. The oil-based lubes, including most massage oils, tend to be a bit "heavier" and to stay slippery longer. Unfortunately, they break down latex products such as latex condoms and gloves. (Oil-based lubes can, however, be used with polyurethane products such as the Avanti condom and the Reality female condom.) Some women report yeast infections following the use of particular lubes; oil-based ones seem to cause more frequent problems. Water-based lubes are generally "lighter" and don't stay slippery as long, but this is easily fixed by adding a few drops of saliva or water. Flavored "lickable" lubricants are good for enhancing oral sex, particularly fellatio (a previous lover of mine relished the "hot cinnamon" flavor), but might be too sugary for penetration or cunnilingus.

Lubricants come with and without nonoxynol-9. This product is marketed as a spermicide and works well in that role. It also kills various microorganisms. Nonoxynol-9 was at one time thought to play a role in the prevention of sexually transmitted disease, but considerably more people than initially thought seem allergic to it, and its use has fallen out of favor.

Some lubricants contain local anesthetics such as lidocaine and benzocaine. These reportedly delay ejaculation and make anal intercourse easier. How useful they are in delaying ejaculation is debatable, and several authorities strongly recommend against their use in anal play. The rectum can be a delicate place. If some activity is causing pain, they feel you need to pay attention to this, not ignore it. Therefore, the use of lubricants containing a local anesthetic is not recommended for easing the difficulty of anal intercourse. (Use more lube instead.) There is a possible use for them in regard to oral sex, and this is covered in the "Tricks" section.

These are just a few of the major points regarding the more common toys. There's much more to learn. Feel free to browse in the store for a while, soaking your brain with knowledge.

A Few Don'ts Regarding Tricks

1. Don't spend too much time doing Tricks. It's far more important to stay in the here and now with your lover. Do a Trick "every now and then."

2. Don't try to do too many different Tricks in a single session. Again, that can distance you from your lover.

3. Don't be overly concerned with looking for opportunities to do a Trick. Let such opportunities appear naturally during the course of events. Men seem particularly vulnerable to this pitfall, thus giving rise to the somewhat bitter saying among many women, "There were three of us in bed: him, me, and his technique."

4. Never place anything in a woman's vagina if it's recently been in her (or, for that matter, any other person's) anus. Doing so can cause her to get an infection that will require a visit to a doctor and antibiotics to cure. For example, inserting your a dildo or your penis into her anus and then into her vagina would be very likely to cause such an infection. (A physician once told me that licking a woman's anus and then licking her vulva could cause her to get infected.) Anything used for anal play must first be thoroughly cleaned before it can be used for vaginal play.

5. Never seal your mouth over a woman's vagina and blow air into it. There are reports of women suffering fatal air

embolisms from this practice. Menstruating women seem to face a considerably higher-than-average risk. Such incidents are very, very rare, but they do happen.

6.   Be careful about placing food items, especially sugary foods, in a woman's vagina. Many men and women recommended placing various foods in there and then eating them out (grapes had something of a cult following). These food can upset the vagina's natural pH balance and cause infections, particularly yeast infections. You can do such Tricks if you want, but if you do, then understand that you may have to deal with their effects "the morning after."

Egg Cream

The bullet- or egg-shaped vibrators are the smallest
types. Tricksters report that inserting one *deep* into her
vagina before intercourse can be great fun for both parties.

Sofa, So Good

While using a dildo on yourself can be very pleasurable,
it can be limiting to have one hand occupied.
Try attaching the dildo to the leg of a couch or heavy chair,
just a few inches above the floor. Then lie on your back, scoot
yourself down "onto" it, and relax, with both
hands now free for other activities.

Jingle Balls

Anal intercourse may be made more pleasurable for her (and
thus for him, too) if she inserts a pair of ben wa balls into her
vagina before being anally penetrated. The brass-within-
plastic type has a particular following.

:4: I Surrender

Insert an egg-type vibrator that has a long cord into your vagina, then hand the control box to your partner. Let them take charge of what sensations you feel, and when.

:5: I'm Pickin' Up Good Vibrations

One way to make a vibrator less threatening to your partner is to offer to give them a massage with it. It feels wonderful to many folks on the tense muscles between the shoulder blades and across the mid-back, for example. If their feet are sore, try a vibrator foot massage. Trade off the vibrator with traditional massage hand strokes.

:6: Sunny Side Up

Another use for a vibrator, particularly a smaller type such as the bullet or egg, is for her to hold it in place on her clitoris during intercourse.
I'm advised that doing so has the potential to produce "a real screamer" of an orgasm for her.

:7:

Chilly Con Carnal

Place the small, all-metal ben wa balls in the refrigerator (*not* the freezer!) at least an hour before sex, then insert them into your vagina just before he enters you. Actually, almost any metal toy – chains, cock rings, what-have-you – can be "chilled out" this way for an interesting sensation. A bowl of ice water kept by the bed can also be useful here.

:8:

Cheek to Cheek

Take his penis into your mouth, then apply a vibrator to your cheek. Move the vibrator sensously from one cheek to the other. Touch it to your lips. Apply it to the point of your chin. Turn your head so that the head of his penis makes a bulge in one of your cheeks and apply the vibrator to that bulge.

:9:

No Holes Barred

Another way that anal intercourse can be made more enjoyable for the woman is if a vibrator is used in her vagina at the same time. Try different sizes and types of vibrators, as well as inserting them either before or after she has been entered.

∴10∴
Stir Well and Serve

Instead of pressing the vibrator directly onto her
clitoris, try circling around it. Vary the speed with
which you make these circles, and the direction,
and the amount of pressure you're applying.

∴11∴
Magic Fingers

Insert two fingers into her vagina, then twist and
thrust them in various pleasurable ways.
Now apply the vibrator to the base of
your fingers and repeat.

∴12∴
Not-Too-Hot Sex

Plug-in type vibrators often heat up during extended use.
If your vibrator has been turned on for a while, touch the head
– especially any metal parts – with the backs of your fingers to
make sure that it hasn't gotten too hot to apply to your
partner. (By the way, several Tricksters
caution that the vibrators which have a heating
element in them are nice for body massage but get
dangerously hot for genital play.) Most plug-in vibrators are
not built to be kept on for a long time, and will burn out if
they're allowed to run too long. Smart Tricksters who enjoy
extended play therefore keep *two* vibrators so they can trade
off when things get a bit too warm.

It Keeps Coming, and Coming...

It is, of course, a very good idea to keep spare batteries
on hand. An Urban Myth states that batteries last
longer if kept in the refrigerator. Studies show this is not true
to any substantial degree. What seems more important is that
the batteries be kept dry – and the average refrigerator is a
very humid environment. Storing your extra batteries in a
cool, dry place, such as the floor of your bedroom closet, is a
much better idea. Also, battery packages come with expiration
dates, so it's easy to keep track of when replacement is
needed.

14

It's a Hit

Hold the vibrator slightly above her vulva, turn it on,
then lightly tap her there. Wait a few seconds, then
repeat the tap. Increase, then decrease, the frequency of the
taps. Increase, then decrease the forcefulness of the taps.
Stay alert for feedback from your parner. The welcome degree
of force can vary from mild and infrequent to heavy and
frequent.

.15.

"Hey, Mabel, What's Wrong With the TV?"

Any device that converts electrical energy into mechanical energy, such as a drill, saw, refrigerator, or vibrator, can interfere with nearby radio or TV reception. This is particularly true if the TV and the vibrator are on the same electrical system - as they might be in a house or apartment building. To help cut down on any possible problems, go to a local electronic store and purchase an inexpensive AC line filter. Plug your vibrator into the filter and the filter into the wall socket. Another possible option is switching to a battery-operated or rechargeable vibrator.

.16.

Watch Your Legs

While using a vibrator is often a great source of pleasure, there are a few conditions that warrant caution. Be careful about using a vibrator if you have been diagnosed with phlebitis, or of using it on unexplained pain in your calf or thigh. You don't want to jiggle a blood clot loose that could travel to your lungs and cause a pulmonary embolism. Those can be as serious as a heart attack. Also, be careful about using a vibrator on swollen or inflamed skin, particulary if you have some medical condition that causes decreased sensation in these areas.

•**17**•
Slip-N-Slide

Many lady Tricksters report that a vibrator
feels too harsh on their clit or vulva without
lubrication. Try applying a nice coat of water-based
lube to one or both before you begin.

•**18**•
Drop & Mop

Ever had trouble at the end of a session remembering which
toys need to be cleaned? A simple solution: When you're
through using a toy, drop it on the floor. (If you're not sure
whether you might want to use it again during the same
session, spread a clean cloth or T-shirt on the floor where
you're going to drop it.) At the end of the session, anything on
the floor gets whisked away to the bathroom or kitchen for
cleaning.

•19•
Keeping Time

Have her lie on her back, and sit between her legs with the
base of the vibrator
in your hand. Place your hand on the bed, then
move the head of the vibrator in an arc from one of her thighs
to the other, crossing over her vulva as you
make the swing. You can vary the degree of pressure,
the amount of time you take to make each arc, and the length
of the arc. One sneaky "tease tactic" is to start by making
very   large, light, slow arcs and gradually make them
smaller, heavier, and faster.

•20•
Stuff & Roast

If you enjoyed the Spanking Tricks in "Tricks
2," imagine how much more you'd enjoy them with a
butt plug in place! The spanker may want to try landing a
couple of smacks, *gently* at first, right on the butt plug, to
provide an extra "jolt" of stimulation. (Watch out for the
tailbone.)

21
Cool Vibes

Yes, it's yet another ice cube Trick.
In this one, stimulate her outer and inner labia with an ice cube (try the cube against your moistened finger first to make sure it's not so frozen that it will stick to her moist tissue) as you apply a vibrator to her clitoris.

22
Two-Timing

If one vibrator is good for her, two may be even better. Try putting one into her vagina and applying a second to her clitoris.

23
The Magical Vibrating Weenie

Grab that vibe, guy, and hold it against the base of your cock while she performs fellatio on you. Why should she be the only one to have vibrator fun?

24

Coordination Challenge

While your partner is sitting on the bed or chair and you're kneeling at their feet performing oral sex, keep yourself entertained by using a vibrator on your own genitals. Careful – don't bite them when you come!

25

Fading In & Out

Slowly bring the vibrator close to their penis or vulva until it's just barely touching. Continue pressing until the pressure becomes very strong. Then slowly reduce the pressure until the vibrator has once again lost touch with their skin. ❧ An alternative approach is to leave the vibrator off while you apply gradually increasing pressure. Once you get to the "medium" level, suddenly turn it on. Then slowly continue to increase the pressure. If the vibrator has different speeds, you can experiment with different pressure levels and different vibration settings.

26

By Yourself

One fundamental rule regarding sex toys that
you buy for yourself is to try them solo before trying them
with a partner. This is often true even if
you and your partner are very intimate and close. "Getting to
know" a sex toy is an extremely personal experience. Things
may go better if it's "just the two of you" for your first few
encounters.

27

A Vibrator Built for Two

Several Tricksters mentioned that if the woman uses a (strong)
vibrator on the front of her vulva, below her pubic bone –
sometimes called the external g-spot – during doggy-style
intercourse, he can feel the vibrations, too. One lady
mentioned, "This is a great, non-threatening way to get him
used to including the vibrator in mutual play, because there's
something in it for him too."

.28.

Butterfly Season

There are several different styles of butterfly-type vibrators on the market under various names. Basically, a butterfly is a shield-shaped vibrator made of soft latex or jelly-like material, usually with the power pack attached via a long cord. It comes with narrow elastic straps that go around her thighs and/or waist, holding it in place against her vulva. In addition to using the butterfly for self-play, some lady Tricksters like to wear theirs during doggy-style vaginal or anal intercourse. Some also enjoy wearing a butterfly during vaginal or anal intercourse while she lies on her back with her legs over his shoulders.

.29.

Up Against the Wall

In this slightly yoga-like Trick, she lies on her back on the floor, bending herself into a letter "L," with her bottom close to a wall. She lifts her legs up on the wall and uses the wall to brace a vibrator either inside her or resting on her clit. (Some folks feel that the legs-up position increases blood flow to the genital area, enhancing the sensations there.)

30.
Pat the Doggie

A lady who is getting happily spanked in a standing, bent-over or doggy-style position may express even more enthusiasm if she's allowed to use a vibrator on her clit during the spanking. (In fact, your hand or arm might wear out before her backside does.)

31.
Outlook Hot & Wet

Apply some "hot" lotion to his penis – the type that feels warmer when you blow on it. (Not Ben Gay or something similar.) Now put one or two ice cubes, or some crushed ice, in your mouth and fellate him.

33.
The Cheek Stretcher

Place a small, bullet-shaped vibrator in your cheek, then give him head. To reduce clean-up hassles, first drop the vibrator into an unrolled, unlubed condom, then tie a knot in the condom behind it.

:34:
G Whiz!

Many people call the g-spot the "female prostate." Whether or not that's anatomically correct, it's functionally correct when it comes to vibrators. The g-spot attachment for a wand vibrator – a plastic cap, with a long crooked "finger," that snaps on over the vibrator head to access those hard-to-reach places – does a wonderful job stimulating the male prostate. (Not sure which way to insert it? If he's lying on his back, put it in so that the "finger" is crooked upwards, toward his penis, against the front wall of his rectum. When you hit the prostate, his reaction should be quite noticeable.)

:35:
A Cup of Silicon To Go, Please

Many coil vibrators come with a "cup" attachment that's supposed to go over the head of a male cock. Most men I've talked to don't get much out of this type of vibration. However, the cup attachment does a good job holding a properly sized silicon dildo – and silicon transmits vibrations very well.

36

Deeper Throat

If you're having problems performing fellatio because of your gag reflex, try applying a local anesthetic to suppress it. Benzocaine, a good one, is found in a number of sore throat lozenges and is one of the main ingredients in Pleasure Balm. Apply some to the back of your throat, wait ten to fifteen minutes, then enjoy.

36

Pearls Are So Versatile

Insert some brand-new or *extremely* clean anal beads, or perhaps a string of pearls (make sure the clasp stays outside), into her vagina. Then insert a vibrator alongside them, turn it on, and enjoy.

37

Pearls Are So Versatile #2

Drape a string of pearls across her clitoris, hold them firmly in place, and touch the vibrator to them. Experiment with varying the sensation from mild buzzing to vigorous bouncing.

:38:
Wonderful Wipes

Diaper wipes make excellent toy cleaners, particularly for the initial clean-up immediately after a session. They often contain alcohol and nonoxynol-9, so a quick swab of a toy with a diaper wipe right after the session is over can make the more "formal" cleaning up later on go easier.

:39:
An Interesting Speculation

Insert a vaginal speculum (inexpensive clear plastic ones are available in some erotic boutiques) and open it wide, then touch a vibrator to it. The sensations will be transmitted throughout the vaginal walls.

:40:
Press the Button

Many women enjoy having the vibrator pushed against their clitoris or pubic mound harder than you might imagine. Try slowly increasing the pressure and see how she reacts.

:41:

Bag of Tricks

If you're playing away from home, pack a few one-gallon zip-lock bags in with your sex toys. Any toy that needs cleaning goes into the bag so you can carry it home without dirtying your other toys. (Some sex party givers have started putting these bags out along with their other safer sex supplies for exactly this purpose.)

:42:

Playing Chopsticks

Combine a long, narrow, rigid implement such as a chopstick with a strong vibrator to vibrate into tiny little places, or to sharply localize the vibration to a larger place. Hold the chopstick loosely in one hand with its tip against the part you want to stimulate, then touch the vibrator to its base.

:43:

Wrist Twist

Many Tricksters swear by the so-called "Swedish" vibrators – the ones that attach to the back of the hand, thus turning your entire hand into a vibrator. However, some people find that fastening one of these toys to the back of the hand and using that hand for genital stimulation runs a risk of painfully pulling pubic hair. If you have this problem, try attaching the vibrator to your wrist instead.

44

Cubes & Balls

Put an ice cube (one with no sharp edges or corners) in your hand, and apply your hand to his well-lubricated penis. Now touch a vibrator to the base of his penis while you masturbate its head. (If you're using a plug-in vibrator, be *very* careful that no part of the vibrator except its plastic head gets wet.)

45

The Layered Look

You probably already know by now that using a toy first for anal play, then for vaginal play, is a great way to start a serious vaginal infection. Multifaceted Tricksters place two or even three condoms or gloves over a vibrator or dildo, then simply remove one barrier in order to move the toy from anus to vagina. (They find that the dildo doesn't mind the loss of sensation too much.)

46

The Waterproof Vibrator

Pull a condom entirely over a (battery-operated only, please!) vibrator and tie the end in a knot. You now have a vibrator that you can take into a hot tub, bathtub or shower.

.47.
Dunk-N-Doze

Hopping out of bed after great sex to go scrub and sanitize your toys is not most people's idea of fun. Some Tricksters keep a bowl or bucket of cleaning solution (see "How To Clean Toys After Use") by the bed and just drop their dunkable toys in to soak as they snooze blissfully. If you're using a bleach solution or some other strong-scented concoction, you may want to keep the receptacle covered or stow it in a nearby bathroom.

.48.
Rotary Sander

When inserting a dildo, vibrator, or similar hand-held object into your partner's rectum, keep in mind that twisting, spinning motions may be considerably more abrasive to the rectal lining than regular in-and-out motions. The more twisting you do, the less time your partner may be able to handle anal play – no matter how much lubricant you use.

•49•

The Postman Rings Twice

There have been several incidents in which a man had great difficulty removing a metal cock ring once it was in place. Try using a rubber cock ring of the same, or perhaps even slightly smaller, circumference. If you can get that one on and off easily, you probably will have little trouble with the metal one.

•50•

Staying At the Y

Butt plugs (particularly those of smallish circumference) have the nasty habit, with only the slightest encouragement from a cough or contraction, of making rather dramatic projectile exits. Unless your scene involves "target practice," consider the following: acquire two strips of one-inch leather (as long as needed). Tie one around your partner's waist. Split the second one down the middle halfway so it forms a "Y" shape. Tie the unsplit end to the back so it acts as a thong/g-string nestling in the crack of the buttocks covering the anus, thus holding the plug in. The "Y" section can then part and go around either gender's genitals to be tied to the waist strap in front, leaving either pussy or cock free for further machinations.

:51:

Thuck Me, Baby!

Touch a small, battery-operated vibrator to the underside of
your tongue during oral sex, thus turning your tongue into a
vibrating sex toy.

:52:

Ring-A-Ding-Ding

Metal cock rings can set off metal detectors, as can ben wa
balls. Keep this fact in mind when traveling to airports,
courthouses, and other places where metal detectors are in
use – or you may find yourself having to make some very
embarrassing explanations.

:53:

What Could Ever Come Between Us?

When using a strap-on dildo, the rubber or
silicone base can be abrasive, or pull on the wearer's pubic
hair. A small piece of soft leather, cut to shape,
can be placed between the mons and the dildo
base to ease this friction a bit.

:54:
Neatness Counts

To dispose of your various safer sex supplies after you're done playing, try this Trick. While still wearing a glove, remove any condoms that need to be removed, pick up any tissues, etc., and hold them in the palm of your still-gloved hand. Now remove the glove by turning it inside out. Tie a knot at the base, and everything will be enclosed therein.

:55:
Leather and Rubber

All you leather-lovers out there probably already know that insertable toys made of leather, such as dildoes, can be very hard to clean. It's therefore especially important that these be covered with a condom before they're inserted (or else kept for use on only one person and only one orifice, and cleaned as best you can afterwards).

.**56**.

Backing Up

The initial entry of anal intercourse is often the most painful part for the receptive partner. This pain can often be minimized by holding the plug or dildo stationary and letting them "back" onto it at their own pace. Entry can also be made easier if the receptive person bears down (as they do when having a bowel movement) while the object is inserted. ❧ Tricksters who enjoy using butt plugs on themselves often set the plug down, business end up, on a chair or toilet seat cover, and gradually lower themselves onto it. One "vertically challenged" lady I know finds the average chair too high for this maneuver, so she likes to place her plug between her bottom and the outside (external) corner of her shower stall, then back onto it.

.**57**.

Gone But Not Forgotten

Even if the battery in your phallus-shaped vibrator is completely dead, or the vibrating mechanism has given up the ghost, it can still give her hours of pleasure used as a dildo. (Many women report that their orgasms feel considerably more satisfying if there's something in their vagina when they come.) Simply inserting it and leaving it there while you masturbate her or perform cunnilingus can make a very pleasant difference.

.·58· .
When Push Comes to Shove

Take the tip of your vibrator and place it between their
genitals and their anus (the perineum). Turn it on,
and begin to press there. Build pressure until
it's almost painful, then slowly back off.

.·59· .
Give Her a Hand

Reach between her legs from above and place your
hand over her vulva, with her clitoris at the
bottom center of your palm. Then
touch the vibrator to the back of your
hand. Experiment with different degrees of
pressure and different vibration settings.
(This can be a good way to cushion the
sensation of a vibrator that feels too strong.)

.·60· .
Waste Is A Terrible Thing to Mind

Be careful where you dispose of your used condoms, gloves,
diaper wipes, tissues, etc. Small children and pets may find
such items, left in an open wastebasket, quite inviting – and
latex goods can be a strangulation risk as
well as a possible source of disease transmission.

.61.

Juggling Balls

Encircle the top of his scrotum with your thumb and forefinger. Squeeze this ring together until it's snug and his testicles are "trapped" below it, then slowly pull down until the skin of his scrotum is pulled tight over his testicles. Now, apply your vibrator to the tight-skinned sack. (Note: pulling down too quickly, too long, or too hard could cause damage; be sure to get feedback from him.)

.62.

Reduce the Richter

Sometimes even the lowest setting on a vibrator produces vibrations that feel too strong. If this happens, try wrapping a towel around its head.

.63.

Frothing at the Mouth

Take a sip of champagne or a soft drink, hold it in your mouth and insert his penis. (This maneuver itself can be very intense.) Now touch a vibrator to your cheek and notice his reaction.

.64.
Squeeze & Shake

Squeeze your genital muscles tightly, then apply the vibrator
to your genitals. Hold the squeeze for
three to five seconds, then release, and remove the vibrator.
Wait a few seconds, then repeat.

.65.
Heartfelt Sigh

Apply the vibrator to the "tender bit" of your
choice, then bring your mouth in close and let
your hot breath accompany the
vibration. Back away a foot or so and
blow a jet of cooler air onto the area. Go
back in close, lick the area to moisten it (if it's
not already wet), and repeat the process.

.66.
Wet & Wild

Soak a washcloth with warm-to-hot (not too hot!) water and
squeeze out the excess. Apply this cloth to the genitals: wrap
it around his penis or place it on her vulva. Press a battery-
operated vibrator to the cloth.

.67.

Seismic Mountain

The "Climb the Mountain" Trick described in "Tricks" and "Tricks 2" can also be done with a vibrator. It's a particularly useful Trick if you know that the recipient can reach orgasm from vibrator stimulation. Apply the vibrator for ten seconds, then remove it and caress the genitals sensously for ten seconds. Re-apply the vibrator, this time for eleven seconds, followed by ten seconds of sensuous caressing. Then apply it for twelve seconds, followed by ten seconds of sensous caressing. ☙ This Trick, alternating ten seconds of sensual caressing with ever-lengthening periods of more arousing genital stimulation, can cause a very slow build-up to a very powerful orgasm.

.68.

Smooth Operator

Sharp edges on a dildo, vibrator, or butt plug do not bear thinking about - but manufacturers aren't always as careful as they should be, and there have been reports of cuts. Inspect a new sex toy carefully before you use it for the first time. Use sandpaper, a nail file, or an emery board to file down any sharp or rough areas.

:69:
The Lazy Daisy

This intercourse Trick offers a pleasant and relaxing way to integrate a vibrator into your sex play. In it, both partners lie spoon-like on their left sides and he enters her from the rear. She then twists her upper body so that she's lying on her back from the waist up, with his head at the twelve o'clock position and hers at about the two o'clock position. They then have intercourse while she uses a vibrator on herself. This position also allows eye contact at the moment of orgasm. ❧ This can be a good position for intercourse if the man is tired. It can also be a good position if one partner is heavier than the other or if one or both parties is full from having recently eaten a heavy meal.

:70:
Brrrrrrr!

One simple but very effective vibrator trick is to apply an ice cube to one of your partner's "tender bits" and then touch the head of the vibrator to it.

·71·
Soft Vibrations

Combine the touch of fur with the touch of a vibrator. Lightly
drape a piece of soft fur – or fake fur if you don't like to use
animal products – over the vibrator's head.

·72·
They Don't Make Band-Aids
Flexible Enough

There are occasional reports of injuries from the
use of a male sheath attached to a vibrator.
These sheaths sometimes have sharp or rough edges from
careless manufacturing, and the strength of the vibration may
mask the injury. A lady Trickster therefore
advises that you first check the interior carefully with your
fingers before inserting your cock. "This is a good rule of
thumb for any cavity," she quips.

·73·
One Jacket, Size Small

It's always wise to cover a butt plug with a condom before
inserting it. However, small plugs are difficult, if not
impossible, to adequately protect this way.
One elegant solution is to put the entire butt plug into a
condom and knot the end behind it.

74

No Fuzz Here

A wise lady Trickster advises against using ordinary towels to dry off toys that are used for insertion. She's had too many reports of lint becoming attached to the toy and causing problems the next time it's inserted. She advocates simply letting the toys air-dry instead. ❧ She also advises placing the toys on a T-shirt to dry instead of on a towel. Again, they're less likely to acquire lint that way.

75

Size Does Matter

A favorite general type of Trick is to have a vibrator in one orifice while his cock is in the other. I hear consistent reports that a smaller vibrator works better in the anus if the cock is in the vagina and a larger vibrator works better in the vagina if the cock is in the anus (particularly during doggy-style intercourse).

186

76

Dot's Right

One wise lady Trickster reduces the chances of acquiring an
anal-to-vaginal infection by reserving some toys only for anal
play and others only for vaginal play. (She does this even
though she is quite diligent about cleaning her toys after using
them.) She tells them apart by marking the ones used for anal
play with a dot of red nail polish on a part of the toy that
doesn't get inserted.

77

A Hole Separate Thing

This same Trickster also stores her anal toys and her vaginal
toys in physically separate locations. That way, she reduces
the chances that an anal toy will accidentally contaminate a
vaginal toy by coming into physical contact with it.

78

If It's Empty, Fill It

Many of the attachments that come with vibrators, such
as g-spot stimulators, are made of hollow plastic. A
knowledgeable Trickster tells me that if you fill up the hollow
places with silicon caulking compound, the toy will have a
warmer, more lifelike feeling.

:79:
Hair You Are

Some Tricksters enjoy the "bristly" sensation
created by attaching a hairbrush to a vibrator. Be careful this
doesn't get so intense that it actually scratches the skin.
(This even feels good on your scalp!)

:80:

Wetter on the Dryer

For   this trick, you'll need a dildo that has a suction cup
on its base, a clothes dryer, some tennis
shoes, and a few towels. Attach the
dildo to the top of the dryer so that it's
sticking straight up. Toss the tennis shoes
and the towels (they can be wet if you like)
into the dryer. Then climb onto the dryer (be
careful!), lubricate the dildo as needed and slide
yourself onto it. Turn on the dryer and enjoy the ride. The
tennis shoes will provide "jolts" that will rock the dryer in a
pleasant way and the towels will muffle the sound somewhat.

·81·

Little Douche Coup

Several lady Tricksters report that they can decrease their
odds of getting a yeast infection after a sex toy and/or
lubricant session by douching soon afterwards. Preferred
douching solutions vary: some recommend using a medicated
douche, while others feel that a simple water and vinegar
douche (a couple of tablespoons of vinegar in a standard-sized
douche bag or bottle) is adequate.

·82·

Cleanliness Is Next To...

Feeling horny and grungy at the same time? Try attaching a
suction cup dildo to your shower wall (be careful of slippery
shower floors). "It's a great way to wake up in the morning,
particularly if you've given up caffeine," says the Trickster
who gave me this idea.

·83·

When You've Outgrown Your
Rubber Ducky

Toy cleaning always seems like a bit of a chore to me,
but one Trickster suggests an easy solution: when she showers
off after play, she takes the dunkable toys that have been
used on her into the shower to clean them.
(If you don't have a shower planned right away, toss the toys
into the stall or tub to wait for you.)

84
Sticky Lips

Be careful about getting lipstick onto a
silicone dildo during dildo-sucking games,
or while putting a condom on one with your mouth.
The color can be very difficult to remove.

85

Patience Is a Virtue

If a woman says it hurts when you thrust a dildo or
vibrator (or a penis) into her, it might mean
that its tip is hitting her cervix.
Consider the following possible remedy.
Under normal circumstances, her cervix
may protrude into her
vaginal canal. However, when she becomes
aroused, muscles deep in her abdomen lift her cervix up
and away from the canal, and often even cause a slight
hollow to form at the end of the canal. ❧ Therefore, if
penetration hurts, try stimulating her clit until
she's more aroused, then try again.

.86.
Two, Two, Two Vibes in One

Put one vibrator into her vagina and another into her anus.
(Don't switch them back and forth.) Alternate strokes with
them, or move them in and out at the same time. Try turning
them on one at a time, then both together. Vary the lengths of
time each one is on. Combine this with masturbating her or
performing oral sex on her.

.87.
Jelly for One

Latex or soft "jelly" dildoes can be very absorbent – soap,
bleach, and other materials can be drawn in and be hard to
remove – so consider carefully which cleaning solution to use.
One Trickster recommends that such a toy be used *only* on one
particular person, then cleaned with large amounts of warm
running water *only* and allowed to air dry.

.88.
Give Her Some Lip

Grab her outer labia and pull, gently but firmly, down
towards her feet. Hold both labia in one hand. Once they're
pulled taut, apply the vibrator to her labia, or to your hand,
or alternate between the two.

.89.

No-Expiration Date

Got a hot date tonight? Make "put fresh batteries in toys" part
of your pre-date checklist. Battery failure at the height of
passion can be sooooo disappointing.

.90.

Sweet Thang

Many women report that using sex toys increases the number
of   yeast infections they get. Sometimes the culprit is
not the toy itself, but the accompanying
lubricant. Many lubricants, particularly
"flavored" lubricants, can cause
infections if used internally. As the old
saying goes: "Sugar grows yeast." Read the
lubricant's label carefully. If it contains
fructose or corn syrup, that may be what's causing the
infection; avoid internal use.
(Sorbitol usually causes no problems.)

91

Sweet Thang #2

Women who report an increased number of yeast infections following the use of a lubricant during vaginal sex might consider that the problem may be with the glycerin.

If I read my medical books correctly, glycerin ($C_3O_3H_8$) is actually a sweet-tasting, syrupy, trihydric alcohol more properly called glycerol and widely used as a lubricant. Glycerol may also be a growth medium for yeast, so some women may benefit from using a lubricant that does not contain it. A British-made lubricant called Liquid Silk contains no glycerin and is gaining in popularity.

92

Surfin' USA

Ladies, try lying face down on your wand vibrator, with the shaft under your belly and the head against your pussy. You might enjoy moving your labia and clit with your fingers to bring different "tender bits" into contact with the vibration.

•93•

Ankle Yank

This Trick works well for solo or partner play.
Insert well-lubricated anal beads one by one into the rectum.
Pull one foot in close to the buttocks (this can work in
face-up or face-down positions) and attach the ring at the end
of the beads to a cord tied to the ankle or toe. During
masturbation, you can straighten your leg to pull out the beads
at the moment of orgasm. During partner play, the game is to
turn your partner on so much that they stretch their legs in
ecstasy, thus pulling the beads out for an extra thrill.

•94•

Shake & Bake

With a plug-in vibrator in one hand and a
plug-in hair dryer in the other, you have some
formidable potential at your disposal.
The combination of heat and vibration can be very powerful.
Just be sure to get feedback from your partner. The heat
could become unpleasant if continued too intensely for too
long on any one particular spot.

95

Meet You In the Middle

Insert two fingers into her vagina, then press a vibrator down
onto her abdomen just above her pubic bone,
as though you were trying to push the vibrator down toward
your fingertips. If she enjoys g-spot sensation,
this may put her over the edge.

96

Hot Tip

Try attaching a q-tip to the head of your
vibrator to give an intense local sensation.
Dry q-tips, wet ones and ones made slippery
with oil or lube all feel a little different.

97

StairMaster

Insert a butt plug and/or a vibrator, then walk
up and down the stairs. (Stay near the banister.
You may need to grab it.)

98

Fingers First

While many people like to be anally penetrated by someone
wearing a strap-on dildo, it may not be
smart to rush directly into this activity.

A wise woman who has played this game with many different
partners advises first inserting some gloved fingers. Feel for
any unusual bumps, roughness, or swelling, and watch for any
blood. If the recipient can take two fingers, then try using a
hand-held dildo on them.

If   that goes well, *then* you can try moving
on to the strap-on type.

99

Brush 'Em Brush 'Em
Brush 'Em

Attach a toothbrush to the vibrator. You'll probably
need two rubber bands, spaced at least an inch apart.
Try the "electric toothbrush" on her clit or his
dickhead, or on either of their nipples, or other
"tender bits," for an interesting reaction.
Careful not to let this get *too* intense.

100
Too Darn Hot

Prolonged exposure to low heat, or exposure to high
levels of heat, can damage condoms, latex gloves, and
sex toys. Keep this in mind when deciding where to store
your toys. Don't place them too near a heating duct, radiator,
or similar heat source.

101
Don't Finish Your Finish

Think twice before placing any lubricated item on a varnished
surface (such as a wooden table or chair or a hardwood floor).
The lubricant may dissolve the finish.

102
Bend & Stretch

Tricksters new to anal play can "train" themselves to
accommodate a plug (or a penis). Insert a plug (see Trick 56
for self-insertion ideas) and leave it in for a while, until you
hardly notice it's there any more. Then try easing it in and out
a few times (add more lube if you need it). Many Tricksters
find that they can take a larger plug if they insert it
themselves than they can if someone else does it.

103

Which Vibrator Is for You?

The wide variety of vibrators out there can be confusing. If you're buying a plug-in vibrator, your basic choice is between the wand-type vibrators (shaped like a shaft with a larger head) and the coil-type ones (shaped like a hairbrush with a shaft onto which attachments can be placed). If you're a woman, one possible hint is to notice how you use your fingers when you masturbate. Do you use a wide, side-to-side motion or do you use a more focused up-and-down motion? If you're a side-   to-side kind of gal, try the wand. Up-and-downers may prefer the coil.

104

Shake 'Em Up, Baby

Ladies, you may change your mind about those ben wa balls lying abandoned in your nightstand if you try inserting them before using a vibrator on your clit and vulva.

105
BYOV

If you're playing with someone who has their own
vibrator, use it – not your vibrator – on them.
This is not just good safer-sex practice; many people are used
to their own vibrator and have an easier time getting off with
it than with an unfamiliar kind.

106

Get a Leg Up

Position can matter a great deal when using sex toys,
especially regarding masturbation. Some Tricksters
report that the position of their legs is particularly important:
they can reach orgasm with their legs in one position, but not
in others. They use this to good effect when they want to
prolong (or shorten) their session.

107

I Want a Man With a Slow...

This can be a good Trick if the man has problems with
premature ejaculation. (It also can work quite nicely for
couples having no problems.) Basically, the man thrusts in and
out of the woman *very slowly* while she uses a
vibrator on herself. This may help the man to last
longer and the woman to come.

108

Vibes for Guys

Vibrators aren't just "girl stuff," fellas. Try using a
vibrator on various parts of your genitals – many male
Tricksters enjoy the vibration on their penis
(particularly on the underside just below the head),
their perineum, and the outside of their asshole.
If it's her vibrator you're using, or if you want to use it on
someone else later, cover it carefully with a condom, rubber
glove or plastic wrap, or put plastic wrap over the part of you
you're stimulating.

109

Everything In Its Place

While many women enjoy insertion play with
a standard vibrator, it was not specifically
designed for vaginal insertion. Many report better
results by first inserting their favorite dildo, then touching a
strong vibrator to the dildo's base.

110

Numb and Number

Many women, and some men, report that lengthy use of a vibrator on their genitals causes the area to "numb out" to an annoying degree. Here is a relative scale of "numb out" activities. 🙖 A. Pulling back the clitoral hood and applying the vibrator directly to the clit produces the fastest "numb out." 🙖 B. Applying the vibrator through the clitoral hood is slower than A. 🙖 C. Applying the vibrator to the labia is slower than B. 🙖 D. Applying the vibrator to the labia through a light piece of cloth (such as the corner of a handy sheet) is slower than C. 🙖 E. Applying the vibrator after its head has been wrapped in a heavy towel is slower than D.

111

Flrrrrrrrrttt...

One flirtatious lady Trickster likes to put a small vibrator in her purse and take it along on a first date, then arrange for it to "accidentally" go off. "I love seeing the expression on his face when he realizes what he's hearing," she says.

112
Slow In Slow Out

Be sure to remove your anal toy slowly and carefully.
Yanking it out feels unpleasant and could cause injury.

113
They're the Expert

While it may be fun to use your partner's vibrator on them,
please don't feel too bad if they have trouble reaching
orgasm from your ministrations. Many people can
only reach orgasm if they use their vibrator
themselves. So, when that time
comes, hand it over.

114
Feeling Thick

Many women report that shorter, thicker vibrators, dildoes,
and so forth feel better in their vaginas than the longer, more
slender, ones feel. More than a few also prefer a dildo
that has a curve to it.

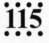 115
Towel Off

Wrap the vibrator in a towel, put it between your legs against
your genitals, and squeeze your legs together for a long count.
Relax for a while, then repeat.

116

Jacket Required for Entrance

While bullet and egg vibrators are not recommended
for anal play – it's too easy to yank the cord loose when you
try to withdraw them – some Tricksters first
place the vibrator in the end of a fully unrolled condom and
then insert it, leaving the base of the condom outside the
rectum to aid in removal. The Reality female condom, with its
inner ring (the one at the closed
end) removed, also works well for this Trick.

117

Who Needs to Be Naked?

A strong vibrator can be excellent for
"real" quickies. You don't even have to
undress, just apply it through your clothing.
As one lady Trickster reported to me,
"It will even go through a snowsuit."

118

Mmmffphth...

Hold the base of the dildo in your mouth
and fuck your partner's mouth with it.

119

Evening Ensemble

Going out for the evening? He can wear his
leather cock ring in the usual way and she can wear an
identical one on her wrist. Nobody but the two
of you will know that you're a "matched set."

120

Whirly Bird

Place a large dildo in a strap-on harness and practice
pelvic thrusts. When you can do "helicopters"
you are really working your pelvic
muscles – toning and trimming for good
sex. (Richard Simmons, eat your heart out.)

121

Who Gloves Ya, Baby?

A condom is a tight fit over the head of a large wand vibrator,
but a glove goes on easily. If you like,
you can wrap and tie a couple of the fingers together
under the head of the vibrator to hold the glove on more
firmly. ❧ If you enjoy a g-spot stimulator with your vibrator,
the thumb of a latex glove stretches easily and neatly over the
"finger" part of the attachment.

122

It's All In the Timing

Many Tricksters enjoy anal play but are grossed out by small amounts of fecal matter on (animate or inanimate) toys. Right after a bowel movement may be a good time to do anal penetration play. If that timing isn't convenient, you may want to try a ready-made drugstore enema about half an hour to an hour before you play.

123

Batteries Not Included

One large adult toy distributor notes that many toys that get returned as "defective" actually just have the batteries put in the wrong way. If batteries in a toy are side-by-side, they should be going in opposite directions. If they're same-end to same-end, they should all be going in the same direction. Also, always remove the batteries from your toys if they're not going to be used for a while (more than a week or so).

124

A Warm Feeling Inside

Applying cold lubricants to sensitive body parts can be momentarily uncomfortable. Many Tricksters recommend placing the bottle of lubricant in some comfortably warm water for several minutes beforehand. (This Trick can also be used on toys that are safe to submerge in water.)

125

When You're Full, Take a Walk

Sex toys don't have to stay at home!
Many Tricksters enjoy the secretive, mischievous
feeling of wearing a dildo or butt plug out in public.
(You should probably avoid doing complex tasks such as driving
a car while you have it in you.)

Latex Allergy

As if we didn't have enough problems, it now appears that far more people are allergic to latex than was previously believed. In a recent paper presented by Dr. Dennis Ownby to the American Academy of Allergy and Immunology, 6.5% of all blood samples at a Red Cross blood bank tested positive for latex allergens. Furthermore, there have been several reports of allergic reactions so strong that they caused the person's death. The FDA has traced at least 16 deaths to severe allergic reactions to latex.

People who are sensitive to latex condoms can try the new Avanti polyurethane condom. (it's worth keeping in mind that such people may not be allergic to the latex, but to the lubricant applied to the latex. Try using a unlubed brand and notice if there is any difference.)

People allergic to latex gloves can try vinyl gloves. Again, some people turn out to be allergic not to the latex itself, but to the powder that sometimes coats latex gloves. Try powderless gloves.

Allergic reactions may dramatically increase in severity from one exposure to the next, particularly if the exposures occur several weeks (or longer) apart.

For very mild, localized allergic reactions, treatment with an anti-inflammatory or antihistamine cream might be all that's required. Creams containing hydrocortisone (anti-inflammatory creams) or diphenhydramine ("poison ivy" creams) will probably work well. Note that neither of these will treat an infection or directly relieve pain. To treat infection, use an antibiotic cream such as

Neosporin or Betadine. To treat pain, use a cream that contains lidocaine or benzocaine. Some creams contain both an antibiotic and an anesthetic.

For moderate reactions, which might involve localized itching, swelling, and inflammation, you might need to take an oral antihistamine in addition to a cream. Diphenhydramine is usually the drug of choice. It's sold under various trade names, including Benadryl and Sominex. I prefer the "sleeping pill" diphenhydramine tablets because they release the drug rapidly into your system. The initial dose of diphenhydramine for adults is 50 mg. by mouth..

For severe reactions, which may involve difficulty in breathing, urgent measures are necessary. Have someone call 911 immediately – this person needs to go to the hospital as quickly as possible.

A drug which specifically counteracts breathing difficulty can be purchased without prescription in almost any drugstore or supermarket. It's called epinephrine (adrenalin) and it's the active ingredient in over-the-counter asthma inhalers.

To use the inhaler, have the patient breathe in the medication, hold their breath for about fifteen seconds, then resume breathing normally. This procedure may need to be repeated a few times. If so, let the patient breathe normally for at least one minute between doses. The patient should not need more than three or four doses, particularly if an ambulance will arrive quickly. Also give them some diphenhydramine tablets. (Give them very little to drink – only enough to get the pills down.)

Diphenhydramine and epinephrine are the two major drugs used in the immediate treatment of severe allergic reactions. They are inexpensive, legal, and widely available. I recommend that you have them with you whenever you're in a situation where someone might have an allergic reaction and medical help is more than just a few minutes away.

Medical/political note: It's possible to purchase, if you have a prescription for it, a self-injecting syringe of epinephrine called an "Epi-pen" or "Ana-Kit." From what I've been able to learn, this costs more and works slower than an epinephrine inhaler, yet I've heard physicians discourage the use of non-prescription inhalers for reasons that sounded more political than medical to me. If you have a serious allergy problem, I'd certainly recommend that you consult a physician regarding the advisability of getting an Epi-pen, but that's something that I'd carry *in addition to* my epinephrine inhaler and diphenhydramine tablets.

If you or your partner has trouble with allergies, spend time down at your local drugstore or supermarket carefully reading the labels and accompanying information on the various creams, tablets, and inhalers. Notice which creams are good for inflammation, itching, infection control and pain relief. (No one cream is good for all four.)

If you know that you have serious allergies, it's crucial to consult a knowledgeable physician. They may be able to administer therapy that will de-sensitize you. Also, diphenhydramine and epinephrine do not mix well with certain other medications – particularly some anti-depressants – and your physician can tell you more about that.

Unfortunately, we are living in a time when more and more people are developing more and more allergies. People with allergies will benefit greatly by learning as much as they can about how allergic reactions develop and what they can do to help manage them. This knowledge can literally be life-saving.

How to Clean Toys After Use

Attempting to "sterilize" a toy is usually neither necessary nor practical. You can, however, remove or kill so many microorganisms that there aren't enough to transmit a disease. (The saying that "it only takes one" is just simply not true. It usually takes several million.) In other words, you can reduce their number below an "infectious concentration" and make it difficult or impossible for them to multiply.

Bugs are just like us in many ways. They need water, protection from extremes of heat and cold, something to eat, shielding from toxins, and a means of reproducing. If any of these gets disrupted too badly, soon the bugs won't exist any more.

Imagine that your favorite sex toy is lying over there on the ground with numerous nasty bugs on it. How might you clean it?

First of all, ask yourself a few questions. They'll determine what approach you take.

Who will this item be used on in the future? If it will only to used on the same person, decontamination isn't such a major issue. (If it's been in her rectum, or if she has a yeast or other vaginal infection, cleaning is difficult, so use a condom on the toy to help prevent further contamination.)

If it will be used on others, it will need a *much* more thorough cleaning. Let's assume it's something you can get wet. First turn on some gently running water. Then put on latex (or other nonporous) gloves, pick up the item, and place it under the stream of water. Be sure no splashing occurs. Let the water run over it for a few minutes. Don't rush. What you're going for here is the physical removal of the bugs. Turn the item until all surfaces are thoroughly exposed.

If the item is absorbent, such as a "jelly" or latex item, and you know that it's only going to be used on the person it was previously used on, you might stop here. Absorbent toys can retain various cleaning agents which can cause irritation or other problems later. Place the item on a low-lint cloth, or other place where it won't pick up any foreign bodies, and allow it to dry.

If the item is nonabsorbent, such as a plastic, silicone, or metal item, rinse it, scrub it with soap for a few minutes, then rinse again. (Simply placing the toy in the top rack of the dishwasher can be an excellent way to accomplish the entire cleaning process.) Don't underestimate the value of this step. A thorough washing with soap and water can remove up to 97% of all bugs.

Soap note: Certain types of soaps kill bugs better than others. In particular, nonscented, liquid soaps containing triclosan (such as "Dial" liquid soap or a generic equivalent) are highly recommended.

Plug-in vibrators and battery-operated vibrators can be wiped with an cloth moistened with bleach solution or alcohol. If you use bleach, a "follow-up" wiping with water or alcohol will be needed to remove any bleach residue. Be sure not to get the "innards" wet.

If you believe that the item needs a more thorough decontamination, you can soak it in a number of cleaning solutions. Remember this principle: *soak for a minimum of twenty minutes.*

Nonabsorbent items can be washed, then soaked in a solution made from nine parts water to one part 5.25% sodium hypochlorite bleach (common household bleach) for at least 20 minutes. This is a very powerful disinfectant with a very broad spectrum. *It is the preferred cleaning agent.* Be sure to use a bleach-water solution that's not more than a few hours old. Rinse with water or alcohol to remove any bleach residue. After rinsing, set it aside to dry.

Nonabsorbent, and some absorbent, items can be soaked for at least 20 minutes in a solution containing at least 60% ethanol or isopropyl alcohol. Alcohol evaporates rapidly, so it may be wise to use a covered container. Note that alcohol is not as broad spectrum a decontaminant as bleach and water.

Metal objects can be boiled for at least twenty minutes. Obviously, other items can't tolerate this degree of exposure to heat.

Leather items such as whips can be very difficult to clean. Wipe them down with soapy water, then wipe them again with alcohol (bleach is more likely to decolorize), and set them aside to dry. They may need to be re-oiled afterwards.

A quiet note about handwashing: more frequent handwashing can do a lot to decrease the spread of infectious disease. (It dramatically reduces the spread of the common cold, for example.) The protective value of washing your hands after you play, and after you clean your toys, is not yet fully appreciated.

Cleaning toys can be something of a chore at first, but with time it becomes "just another part of it." Also, the time spent cleaning your toys can be a delicious time to contemplate how, when, and on whom they'll next be used.

What to Do If You "Lose" Something In the Rectum

Most "formal" anal toys have a wide flange at their base to prevent their being pulled all the way in. Items without a flange, such as ben wa balls, cordless vibrators, and so forth, are not recommended for anal play. Use dildoes that lack a widening at the base only if you can keep a firm grip (with your entire hand, not just a few fingers) on them at all times. Note that the large amount of lubricant required by anal play can make keeping such a grip a definite challenge.

Every now and then, something "vanishes" into the rectum – particularly if it's something not specifically designed for anal play. This vanishing act can happen if a curved part of the rectosigmoid colon suddenly "unbends" a bit or if the item goes in beyond the sphincters.

If this does happen, keep in mind that the item will almost undoubtedly pass back out naturally and on its own before long. The natural peristaltic action of the bowel will prevent the item from working its way farther up. There's no need to mount a dramatic rescue operation. Above all, *don't do anything that hurts*. The item should appear no later than the next bowel movement. Assuming a squatting position, as opposed to the usual sitting position, may help pass the object.

(Caution: mild to moderate bearing down is probably OK. Hard straining could damage the rectal passage – and, particularly if the individual has a heart condition, could possibly slow the heartbeat or even precipitate a cardiac arrest.)

You might be able to reach the item with a fingertip. If so, you may be able to ease it down until you can grasp it and (gently, slowly) extract it. One major caution: be careful not to push the item farther in. Sitting or standing in a upright position, or walking around for a while, may help the item work its way back down to where you can reach it.

Inserting an ounce or two of additional lubricant into the rectum may also help. At this point, a more liquid lubricant (such as mineral oil) is probably better. Careful use of an enema bulb or turkey baster can help ensure that the lubricant goes into the rectum. The individual should lie on their left side as the lubricant is inserted, and for several minutes thereafter, then sit, stand, or walk.

A few don'ts:

1. No enemas, please (other than as mentioned above). Large volumes of water are not what the intestine needs just now. Among other things, the water may push the object further in, where it can *really* get stuck.

2. No stimulant or irritant-type laxatives such as senna, bisacodyl, or castor oil.

A few possible options:

1. Simply waiting is a very rational strategy. There is a good chance that the item will pass out naturally. (If it isn't passed with the next bowel movement, the odds of your having to seek medical aid greatly increase.)

2. Eating a meal can trigger the gastro-colic reflex and thus cause a bowel movement approximately 30 to 60 minutes afterwards, as can drinking a caffeine-containing beverage – perhaps especially a warm, caffeine-containing beverage.

A few warning signs:

1. The person has a prior history of rectal, anal, or other bowel problems. (You *did* check this before you started stuffing things up there, didn't you?)

2. The person develops cramping abdominal pain, other bothersome abdominal pain, fever, or blood starts coming from their rectum. If any of these appear, it's time to see a physician immediately.

3. The object hasn't passed on its own after twenty-four hours. Again, it's now time to see a doc.

Subpoint: If this could happen to you, think for a moment about where you'd go. This may not be something you want on your regular, permanent medical record. A visit to a local free clinic, women's clinic, or other resource may be more appropriate. Your local erotic boutique or SM-oriented leather store may be able to give you the name of a discreet, sex-positive physician. If you have a sex-positive, discreet friend who is a physician, nurse, paramedic, chiropractor, or other type of medical person, you may be able to get advice and/or a referral from them. Also, a sympathetic physician may be found by contacting local sexuality-related organizations such as clubs for gay men, lesbians, bisexuals, transgender people, or SM folks. You may not have to give your real name, but please be open regarding medical information – and pay your bill if at all possible.

It is very wise to have your "plan B" doctor lined up ahead of time. Trying to find such a person while under the stress of an urgent situation can be very difficult. Some stores and clubs keep listings of "friendly" health care professionals. Sexuality author and educator Race Bannon maintains a list of physicians, chiropractors, therapists and other professionals who offer sexually nonjudgmental services; you can visit it at www.bannon.com/kap.

Summary

By far the best way to deal with this situation is to not get into it in the first place. Careful selection and use of toys for anal play will prevent most problems. If something does get lost, remember the odds are that it will find its own way back without too much help from you.

The Five "Shuns" of Anal Play

The anal region has a good supply of nerve endings. Skillfull anal play can be very rewarding, both physically and psychologically. Reports of orgasm from anal play alone are not rare. Still, this is not something that one should rush into.

The anus and rectum are not "intended" for insertion. While fingers, butt plugs, dildoes, vibrators, anal beads, and other items have all been inserted successfully, this area of erotic play requires a high level of awareness.

The various issues of successful anal play can be looked at in terms of the five "tions" (shuns). They are, in the approximate order you'll need them: information, protection, lubrication, relaxation, and communication.

Information

The receptive person should tell their partner about their past experiences (or lack thereof) regarding anal sex, particularly any problems that have occurred. They should also mention any anal or rectal problems they have, such as hemorrhoids, fissures, an enlarged prostate, or more serious medical conditions. (People with heart disease should know that heavy bearing down, during anal play or during a bowel movement, can slow the rate and force of their heartbeat, sometimes to zero. Use appropriate caution and seek medical consultation as necessary.)

Protection

Disease can be transmitted in both directions during anal play. For this reason, barrier usage is very strongly recommended.

Dildoes, plugs, vibrators and penises should be covered with condoms. Hands and fingers should be covered with gloves. Toys and hands should be cleaned afterwards.

Lubrication

The vagina and the mouth supply their own lubrication; the rectum does not. While the vagina sometimes needs a little extra lubrication, the rectum *always* does. In general, "heavier," more gel-like lubricants tend to work better than the "lighter," more liquid-like lubricants. Nowadays, water-soluble lubricants are preferred over oil-soluble lubricants, particularly if latex condoms and/or gloves are being used. Colored or scented lubricants should probably be avoided. Remember: "Lube early; lube often."

Relaxation

While erotic fiction contains many depictions of a person having something shoved suddenly and deeply into their rectum by an uncaring, dominant partner, the reality is far different.

The anus has two rings of sphincter muscle: the external and the internal. The internal takes longer to relax. Start very gently and ease in only one finger. (Placing a cotton ball in the fingertip of your glove can help eliminate any "sharp" feeling.) Use lots of lube, don't move the finger around too much, and pay close attention. You may actually feel the sphincter relax. When you can move one finger in and out easily, add more lube and try slowly inserting a second finger. I recommend you not insert a vibrator or dildo until you can easily thrust two fingers all the way in and out. Having this done to you will teach you a great deal about how to do it to someone else.

Communication

Successful anal penetration requires feedback. Even a small variation in pressure, location, depth, or angle can make a major difference in how well the play goes. The "receiving" partner must communicate these matters clearly and promptly to the "giving" person so necessary adjustments can be made. Above all, the receiving partner shouldn't "tough it out" in silence in order to please their lover. If something feels wrong, it almost undoubtedly is wrong and needs prompt correction. Failure to take corrective action can put the receptive person in the hospital. There are even reports of fatalities. Anal play is *not* the time for the receptive partner to take a "stoic heroic" approach. Ongoing communication and adjustment are essential.

So there are the five "tions" of anal play. One useful way to remember them is to remember that there is one for each finger. Can you name them "off the top of your hand"?

Twenty SM Safety Tricks

I consider SM the riskiest form of sex. It has all the risks associated with "vanilla" sexuality, plus the very real physical, emotional, and relationship risks that go along whenever one person binds, dominates, or "tortures" another.

I have written a comprehensive guidebook to this very rewarding and very risky form of sexuality. It's called "SM 101: A Realistic Introduction" and there's a good chance it's available from the same place that you got this book. All of the matters listed below are discussed in far greater depth and detail in that book. If SM is becoming a serious interest of yours, please consult "SM 101" for more information. There is also a great deal of useful information in the "Spanking Tricks" section of "Tricks 2: Another 125 Ways To Make Good Sex Better."

I have very strong reservations about "quickie" SM instruction, but I have to face the fact that most of the stores that sell this book also sell SM gear such as restraints, blindfolds, gags, clamps, paddles, and whips and such devices are, after all, most definitely sex toys. I'm therefore going to include some basic SM safety precautions in this book. This information is *not* meant to be adequate instruction. Rather, its purpose is to steer you away from the most common, major hazards.

By all means, check out some of the SM books recommended herein. If you can, contact a local SM club for additional instruction. Also, you can find some first-rate educational material regarding SM on the Internet. Check out the newsgroups soc.sexuality.bondage-bdsm, soc.sexuality.bondage-bdsm.femdom, and soc.sexuality.spanking, and use the various World Wide Web search engines to discover the many excellent resources available there.

SM Safety Tricks

1.   Be very careful about who you let tie you up.

You might think that this would be so obvious as to not be worth mentioning. I have found differently. Bondage need not be dangerous in and of itself, but it most definitely is dangerous in terms of the vulnerability it creates. When two people are alone together, that's one degree of risk. However, when two people are alone together and one of them is tied up, the degree of risk dramatically increases. Be very wary of someone who "only" wants to tie you up. You are quite literally trusting them with your life.

I strongly recommend that you let someone tie you up only after you have first done at least two SM-type sessions with them that didn't involve any bondage. While all SM encounters have some risk attached, the first few SM sessions you do with a new partner are by far the ones most likely to "go wrong."

Subpoint: Limit the amount of bondage during the first few times you try it. My general rule is that the first time I let someone tie me (after a few successful non-bondage sessions), I'll only let them tie my hands to each other. I will let them tie my hands behind my back, but I most definitely will *not* let them tie me to something such as a bed or chair. I won't let them tie my elbows, my knees, or my ankles in any way. I also won't allow them to blindfold or gag me the first few times we play together. (Among other things, they're going to need the feedback provided by my voice and facial expressions.)

A common suggestion is "Let's try some bondage. I'll tie your wrists and ankles to the four corners of the bed. It won't hurt." You can see how this involves way too much vulnerability for a first-time session.

2.   Experience it yourself, preferably several times, before you do it to someone else.

The more empathy you have with what the other person is experiencing, the better partner you'll be and the more the both of you will benefit. There's an adage in the SM community that it's better to start out in the "submissive" or "bottom" role. This is true *if* you have access to an experienced, empathetic, ethical partner (lucky you!) and *if* you can assume such a role without too much emotional difficulty. If either is not true, then maybe you're better off not doing that — at least for a while. It is entirely possible and valid to start off in the "dominant" or "top" role.

If doing a "submissive internship" (which can vary widely in its length, intensity, and variety) isn't an option, do what you can to experience what they're experiencing. Try applying that toy to your own body. Try kneeling on the floor yourself for a while. Try staying in the position you want them to remain in while bound. (Be careful about tying yourself up. See later in this book.) The more empathy you have for what the submissive is experiencing, the better dominant you'll be.

3 .   Play with a "Silent Alarm" in place.

When I play privately with a new partner, I always have what's called a "silent alarm" in place. What that means is that somebody I trust knows where I am, who I'm with, and what we're doing. If I fail to check in with this person by a certain time and in a certain way, they will know that I'm in serious trouble and things will start to happen — sometimes up to and including calling the cops. (I'm very serious about this. I have called the cops myself when someone I'm "baby sitting" has failed to check in.)

The primary purpose of a Silent Alarm is *deterrence*, not after-the-fact arrest of the perpetrator. Therefore, I always let my new partner know ahead of time, as diplomatically as possible, that such a device will be in place while we're playing. Furthermore, I urge them to do the same.

A good partner will understand and not be upset or angry about my using a silent alarm. Furthermore, they will *not* question me regarding details of how the alarm is set up. Any show of negative emotion on their part, or any questioning regarding how my alarm works or why I felt the need for it, are major red flags that I should just simply not play with this person, ever. If they are new to the practices of SM, I might politely advise them *one time* that such questions are considered out of line. If they still continue, it's time for me to forget the whole thing.

4.   Use only plain paraffin candles for hot wax play.

Many people are now aware that it's possible for one person to drip wax from a burning candle onto their lover's skin as a from of erotic play. One major word of advice: use *only* plain white paraffin candles. Colored candles, and candles made of materials such as beeswax, may melt at a much higher temperature. People have suffered third degree burns from having such candles used on them. Also, be sure to drip a few drops of that wax onto your own skin (the back of your hand works well) before dropping it onto your lover's skin. Notice how the temperature of the wax varies according to the height from which it's dropped.

5.   Avoid leather toys with sharp edges or corners.

While the equipment sold in "formal" SM stores tends to be of excellent quality, the equipment sold in other stores may not be. In particular, when considering purchasing something made out of leather such as a whip, a collar, or a set of cuffs, check out their edges and corners. A quality piece of equipment will have these places rounded off and smooth to the touch. A shoddy piece of equipment may have amazingly sharp edges and corners. You can imagine how human skin will react to being whacked by something so sharp. If you find such a piece of equipment, tell the store manager that you're not buying it, and tell them why.

6.   Don't whip someone over their kidneys (or liver, or spleen).

While almost any place on the body except the eyes and ear canals can be struck *very* lightly, heavier blows must be confined to the more padded areas. The head, neck, arms, and lower legs (including the knees) are basically just not suitable as targets for a whip. In particular, avoid heavy blows to the abdominal cavity. Place your hands on the crests of your hips. Now place them on the bottom of your breastbone at the notch where your ribs come together (the xiphoid process). You'll want to stay below the hip crests and above the xiphoid process.

The best area on the back for whipping is lower half of the upper half. The best area on the buttocks is the lower half. (The inner, lower quadrant is frequently the most erotic place, and is known in SM circles as the "sweet spot.") As always, experience and feedback are essential.

7.   Clamps hurt most when coming off.

When a clamp is applied to a nipple or to some other tender body part, it compresses the tissue and blood is forced from the area. (This means that the area now has no blood supply. Experts differ regarding how long a clamp should therefore be left on, but their answers are all expressed in terms of minutes, not hours.) When the clamp is removed, blood rushes back into the tissue and re-expands it – and that hurts!

There is nothing that can be done to prevent this pain. It can help somewhat to remember that the acute phase will only last for a period of several seconds (milder residual soreness may last longer), to develop a skilful hand when it comes to removing them, and to remove one clamp at a time, with the submissive signaling when they are ready to have the next clamp removed.

It's wise to experiment with ordinary, inexpensive, spring-type, wooden clothespins before buying more "formal" clamps. While people can vary widely in how they react to having clamps applied to them, as a rule the more experience you have with applying them to, leaving them on, and removing them from your own body the better you'll become regarding using clamps on someone else's body.

8.   Keep it friendly.

Do SM only with people you know well, and are on good terms with, and when you're both in a good mood. Playing SM with a stranger, with someone you're not on good terms with, or when one or both of you is tired, upset, intoxicated, or otherwise not at your best, dramatically increases the degree of risk.

9.   Watch out for their tailbone.

A heavy blow to a person's tailbone (coccyx) can cause a very painful sprain, dislocation, or even fracture of that part of their body. This can be particularly true if they are bent over at the waist. The size, apparent position, and angle of the tailbone can vary quite a bit from person to person. Before giving them a spanking or whipping, take a moment to feel their tailbone. Also, if you move them from a "straightened out" to a "bent over" position, take a moment to feel if it's now more prominent.

10.   Negotiate what you'll do ahead of time.

As I say in "SM 101": "When two people are alone together, and one of them is naked and tied up, and the other is standing over them with their hands full of torture implements, this is *not* the time to have a serious mismatch of expectations." Adult-to-adult negotiation before playing is standard practice among experienced SM practitioners. Indeed, many SM folks pride themselves on their non-manipulative, highly ethical, negotiation skills. (Negotiation is dealt with at great length in "SM 101." There's even a negotiation checklist.)

Negotiations can cover the types and duration, of bondage, what sexual acts will and won't occur, what types of spanking or whipping will or won't occur, and many other matters. Experienced SM people can often conduct a full negotiation in five to ten minutes. Less experienced people may take hours. That's fine. It's far better to do more negotiating than you need to than less negotiating than you need to.

Important subpoint: During the SM play, it's important to stick to the limits set by the pre-play negotiation. It's particularly important that going further than previously agreed not be proposed during the play by the dominant partner.

11. Check in with each other afterwards.

In order to properly deal with the SM session, the people involved need to spend "straight time" (out of role and in a non-sexual context) discussing what happened and their reactions to it. There are three basic check-in times:

Immediately afterwards. No major discussion is usually needed or advisable here. Just a brief reassurance that both parties are basically emotionally and physically OK.

The next day. By now, the participants have had a chance to intellectually and emotionally react to the play. This is the best time for a "debrief" regarding what happened to discuss thoughts and feelings, what worked and what didn't, and so forth. It's also usually the soonest time to discuss if and when the two people involved will play again.

About a week later. This is the time to deal with any emotional "aftershocks" that may have come up. It's also a time to deal with any physical problems that may have not been apparent immediately afterwards or the next day. (Both of these occurrences are rare, but they do happen.)

12. Bondage Safety Tip #1: Loss of sensation.

There is never any need to tie any body part so tightly that it loses feeling. If some part of your lover's body "goes to sleep," then it's time to loosen whatever's causing the problem.

13.   Bondage Safety Tip #2: Quick release.

If you tie someone up, you must have some method of releasing them quickly. That means you must be able to get them completely free within sixty seconds, and preferably within thirty seconds.

One basic safety precaution is to keep a pair of scissors handy so you can cut your lover free in an emergency like a fire or earthquake. The large, plastic-handled "paramedic scissors" popular with rescue squads are an excellent choice because, unlike regular bandage scissors, they were designed to cut through leather, webbing, and other heavy materials quickly. These scissors are available at many medical supply stores. The more health-conscious and responsible leather stores and erotic boutiques also carry them.

Both nylon stockings and silk scarves – often the first choice of beginners – are notoriously difficult to untie if the knots have been pulled really tight. Don't use anything you're not willing to cut through if necessary.

14.   Bondage Safety Tip #3: Stay with them.

Many people think it would be fun to "tie them up and then go off and leave them." In fact, this is one of the most dangerous, irresponsible things you can do. It's a crime in many areas. Furthermore, if your partner is injured in any way while you are gone, even if they asked you to leave them, you could face major criminal charges.

Here's a simple rule: Always stay as close to a bound person, and check on them as often, as you would an infant left in your care. If you gag them, stay even closer and check even more often.

15.   Bondage Safety Tip #4: Emergency lighting.

A bound person needs to be closely watched. In an emergency, they need to be immediately freed. To do both of these in an efficient manner, you need light. A power failure during a normal sexual encounter can be, at the least, annoying. A power failure during a bondage session can be a serious, even life-threatening, problem.

Therefore, responsible bondage fans always make sure they have emergency light sources immediately available. Flashlights, especially light-colored ones that are easy to see, are carried in pockets, stored in specific places in "toy bags," and otherwise placed where they can be easily found in the dark.

Furthermore, increasing numbers of bedrooms and "playrooms" now have "blackout lights" – lights that come on automatically if the power fails – plugged into their wall sockets. Basic models that will do quite nicely for the average-sized room can be bought at drugstores, variety stores, and similar places for around ten to twenty dollars.

16.   Bondage Safety Tip #5: The dangers of self-bondage.

Many people have bondage fantasies but no partner, so they bind themselves. The person interested in self-bondage faces a problem. They want to bind themselves so they can't escape, yet, obviously, eventually they will want release. What to do?

Self-bondage can be extremely dangerous. You know how risky it is to bind someone and then leave them alone. The self-bound person has this obvious problem.

I have heard of several deaths resulting from self-bondage that went wrong. Even more disturbing, many of these deaths involved highly experienced players who "knew what they were doing" yet died anyway. Most such fatalities involved gags, hoods, ropes around the neck, or some other devices that had the potential to restrict breathing.

Most self-bondage involves locking devices, especially around the wrists. The person works out some mechanism by which the keys again come within their grasp. If the device fails to work (and, sooner or later, it *will* fail) the bound person often has no other way to get free or summon help.

Also of critical importance, bondage not tight enough to put the bound area to sleep quickly may still be tight enough to do that gradually. The self-bound person's hands may go numb after an hour. If the keys fall within reach after that – trouble.

I experimented for a while with self-bondage, but gave it up after I had an incident that gave me a moment of nearly pure panic. I also found that, besides its dangers, self-bondage has other drawbacks.

First, you may rapidly discover that being in bondage without a "sweet tormentor" for company is *boring*. The vibrators, clamps, dildoes, and other gear that aroused you when you first put yourself in bondage may feel awful after your arousal fades – even if it doesn't malfunction or go out of adjustment. If, genius that you are, you set the situation up so you can't get loose for three hours, you may find that the last two hours and fifty minutes go on for a *very* long time.

You might try binding your breasts and genitals, but be very conservative about using anything that would restrict your breathing (gags, hoods, neck ropes), make you vulnerable to a fall (blindfolds), or restrict your limbs – especially your arms.

Self-bondage often seems like a good idea in fantasy, and offers plausible exploration, as long as *absolutely nothing* goes wrong. Remember that even a minor maladjustment of a piece of equipment can set the stage for hours of genuine suffering, and that a serious malfunction or unexpected development can cause you to die a slow, agonizing death. Many "experts" died exactly this way.

17.   "One to ten."

Raise your hand about twelve inches above the receiver's buttocks and let it drop. Tell the receiver that the stroke they just received had a strength of three. A "two" is about half that forceful, and a "one" is little more than a very light touch. The strength of the spanks can go all the way up to "ten" with each spank above three being about 25% stronger than the previous number.

Tell the receiver that when they call out a number, it will indicate both the strength of the spank they are willing to receive *and* that they are willing to receive it. Tell the receiver that this number can *both* increase and decrease.

This Trick is very useful in helping the receiver, particularly a novice, retain their emotional balance. They are thus much more likely to open up to and enjoy the experience.

18. Keep "reality" out of it.

Spanking fans often role-play situations (naughty pupil and teacher, disobedient child and baby sitter, etc.) to act out spanking fantasies. These scenarios often involve someone getting "punished" for some supposed "misconduct." All well and good.

However, it's *very* important to keep real world situations out of spanking games. Spanking someone because they forgot to pay the phone bill, left the lights on, or did something similar that you really didn't like, can be a recipe for disaster. Spanking games are consensual, erotic, fantasy play, not a place to settle scores or grudges. Those get handled in "straight time," not in the bedroom.

19. Harder is not necessarily better.

People who enjoy giving and/or receiving spankings vary tremendously in how hard they want their spankings to be, and how often they want to give or receive one. It's important for each individual to find out what works best specifically for them. Just remember: Harder is not necessarily better. More painful is not necessarily better. Longer is not necessarily better. More often is not necessarily better.

20. Two squeezes means I'm OK.

A spanking can create its own intense world for the receiver. Sometimes the giver will want to check on the receiver's well-being without asking a direct verbal question – doing so could spoil the mood, also receivers sometimes "go under" into a deep, non-verbal part of themselves.

A very effective alternative to checking in verbally is for the giver to take the receiver's hand in theirs and give it two firm and noticeable, but not painful, squeezes. Each squeeze should last about one second and there should be about a one-second pause in between them. This is understood to ask the question, "Are you *basically* OK with what's going on here?" The receiver signals back that they are (at least) basically OK with the situation by giving the hand of the spanker two squeezes in return. (It is, of course, essential that you and your partner get clear on this point *before* the spanking actually begins.)

If the spanker squeezes the receiver's hand and gets no reply, they should wait about ten seconds and then repeat the two squeezes. If another ten seconds brings no "reply squeezes," it's time to make verbal contact.

Problems

Probably the most important advice I can give you regarding finding help for the problems listed below, and other problems, is to grab your phone book and start looking. Many communities have local resources. Check the first few pages and look over the table of contents. Look up these and related topics in both the white and yellow pages. Check your phone book for an index.

If this doesn't help much, go to your local library and look through the phone books of nearby communities, particularly those of nearby big cities.

Local newspapers and magazines, particular free or low-cost ones that come out on a weekly or less frequent basis, often carry valuable listings. Gay and lesbian papers can be particularly helpful. Look them over carefully.

The Internet is an excellent source of information regarding sexuality-related problems. Look in the alt.recovery, alt.sex and alt.support hierarchies, in any newsgroups that announce local events and groups in your community, and on the World Wide Web.

Abuse/Battering/Neglect

National Domestic Violence Hotline (800) 799-7233

National Child Abuse Hotline (800) 422-4453

Parents Anonymous (800) 249-5506

AIDS

National AIDS Hotline (800) 342-AIDS

National STD Hotline (800) 227-8922

Birth Control/Abortion

Check your local yellow pages under "Birth Control Information Centers." Note: Some anti-abortion agencies have been accused of being less than totally honest about that fact. If a given resource doesn't explicitly say that it offers abortions, please consider that its policies may be anti-abortion.

Censorship

American Civil Liberties Union
132 West 43rd St.
New York, New York 10036
(212) 705-7496

National Coalition Against Censorship
132 West 43rd. Street
New York, New York 10036
(212) 807-6222

People for the American Way
2000 M. Street N.W., Suite 400
Washington, DC 20036
(202) 467-4999

Death During Sex

People, especially older men, die during sex far more often than is commonly believed. One of the reasons for this is that their partners are often too embarrassed to tell what was going on when the death occurred.

Studies have shown that the person in the community who faces the highest risk of sudden cardiac arrest is a man over the age of 50, and the person most likely to be with him when it happens is his wife. If your boyfriend or husband is over 50, I strongly recommend that you both take a CPR class.

Studies have also shown that the second highest risk group for a sudden cardiopulmonary emergency is, to simplify matters, anyone wearing diapers. If you help take care of young children, schedule a class that teaches infant and child CPR. (The technique differs considerably from that used on adults.)

You can look in the yellow pages under "First Aid Instruction" to find out where classes are offered. The American Red Cross, American Heart Association, some hospitals and emergency service agencies, and private firms all offer classes.

If you take a CPR class, try hard to get a good instructor. I suggest someone who has a minimum of one year of full-time experience in pre-hospital emergency care. A paramedic might be a good first choice. (Although people who are good at providing emergency care are not necessarily good at teaching others how to do that.)

Disabilities

The Lawrence Research Group, which publishes the Xandria Collection catalogs, puts out a specialized catalog of sex toys and advice for people with disabilities. This catalog also contains a page listing of sexuality resources for the disabled across the U.S. To receive this catalog, send $4 and a request for the Special Edition for Disabled People to:

Lawrence Research Group

P.O. Box 319005

San Francisco, CA 94131

Herpes

Herpes Resource Center (HRC)

P.O. Box 13827

Research Triangle Park, North Carolina 27709

These folks offer wonderful information for those coping with any aspect of herpes. Among other things, they sponsor a nationwide network of support groups. If somebody I cared about had herpes, I would make certain that they were fully informed about what these folks offer.

National STD Hotline (800) 227-8922

Incest

Incest Survivors Anonymous
P.O. Box 5613
Long Beach, CA 90805-0613
(310) 428-5599

Survivors of Incest Anonymous
P.O. Box 21817
Baltimore, Maryland 21222
(410) 282-3400

Both of these groups sponsor meetings all over the country. They will also help you start a group in your area if one does not already exist. Incest is one of the most under-reported forms of abuse in this country.

Old Age

Sex Over Forty Newsletter
PHE, Inc.
P.O. Box 1600
Chapel Hill, North Carolina 27515

As people age, their needs and their bodies change. This newsletter is one of the most informative and useful sources of information on the topic.

Rape

As soon as you safely can, call 911, a rape treatment center, or a similar resource. Check your phone book under Rape, Battering, and Sexual Abuse Aid. It's very important from a medical, emotional, and legal point of view to seek help as soon as possible after the assault. Know that an attempted rape can be almost as damaging, and take as long to recover from, as a completed rape.

If you can safely do so, have the authorities come to the scene so they can look for valuable evidence. Try not to shower, douche, brush your teeth, or change clothes until you've been examined.

If you need support or don't feel your case is being handled properly, by all means contact a rape crisis center for more help.

Sex Therapy

You don't necessarily need a formally trained sex therapist to help you cope with sexual problems. Many therapists with broader training do excellent work in this field.

That said, I want to mention that the organizations listed below help train and set policies for sex therapists. Someone representing themselves as a sex therapist would probably have extensive contact with at least one of them.

Sex therapy is not an exact science. In particular, such issues as the use of surrogates are highly controversial. You should understand that the organizations listed below are far from in total agreement on every issue. AASECT is considered the more conservative.

Society for the Scientific Study of Sex (SSSS)
P.O. Box 208
Mount Vernon, Iowa, 52314

American Association of Sex Educators, Counselors, and Therapists (AASECT)
435 Michigan Ave, Suite 1717
Chicago, Illinois 60611

Sex and Love Addiction

These are 12-step groups designed to help people achieve "sexual sobriety" by using the principles of Alcoholics Anonymous. They have chapters in many parts of the country. If one doesn't exist in your area, they will help you start one. (Don't be surprised if your initial outreach efforts draw more people than you expected.)

Sexaholics Anonymous
P.O. Box 300
Simi Valley, CA 93062

Sex and Love Addicts Anonymous
P.O. Box 119
New Town Branch
Boston MA 02258

Suicidal/Homicidal Feelings

Almost every local community has telephone crisis hotlines. Again, check your telephone book – particularly the first few pages.

Additional Resource Information

San Francisco Sex Information, at (415) 989-7374, offers referrals and a sympathetic ear. They most definitely do not, however, offer phone sex.

Alternative Sexuality Resources

As with the "Problems" section, many resources can be found by carefully checking in your phone book and by visiting the library to check the phone books of nearby cities, particularly large ones. Also, many alternative sexuality clubs and other resources advertise in adult papers and other periodicals with an erotic slant.

The internet is also an excellent source of information regarding most forms of alternative sexuality. The majority of sexuality newsgroups fall under the alt.sex hierarchy, but some, typically more oriented toward philosophy, politics and discussion, can also be found in other hierarchies such as soc.*. The World Wide Web also includes a huge number of pages with information, articles, photographs and resource lists on various alternative sexualities.

Important Notice: When writing to any of these organizations, it's wise to include a business-sized, self-addressed, stamped envelope.

Bisexuality

Bisexual Resource Center
Robyn Ochs
P.O. Box 639
Cambridge, MA 02140
(617) 424-9595

Body Size and Weight

National Association to Advance Fat Acceptance (NAAFA)
P.O. Box 188630
Sacramento, CA 95818

A national support organization, with chapters in many cities, for fat people and their admirers.

Circumcision

NOCIRC (an anti-circumcision organization)
P.O. Box 2512
San Anselmo, CA 94960

Corsetry

For people who enjoy wearing corsets and people who enjoy people who enjoy wearing corsets.

B.R. Creations
P.O. Box 4201
Mountain View, CA 94040
Ask about their "Corset Newsletter."

Cross Dressing

ETVC
P.O. Box 426486
San Francisco, CA 94142

This is a respected educational and social organization for people exploring gender issues and those who care about them. It publishes a newsletter that contains many local resources, national resources, and information on other local groups around the country. Highly recommended.

International Foundation for Gender Education (I.F.G.E.)
P.O. Box 367
Wayland, MA 01778
(617) 894-8340

The organization publishes the "TV/TS Tapestry Journal," a 150+ page magazine containing articles, references and other resources. Sample copy $12.00. Again, highly recommended.

Expanded Families

PEP
Box 6306
Ocean View, Hawaii 96704-6306
Nationwide organization promoting polyfidelity, group marriage, and expanded families.

Gay and Lesbian Resources

National Gay Yellow Pages ($10.00)
Box 292
Village Station
New York, New York 10014
Again, your local phone book should help you find resources in your area.

Infantilism

Diaper Pail Friends
38 Miller Avenue #127
Mill Valley, CA 94941
This is *not* about adults having sex with children. DPF is an organization for adults who enjoy dressing up and pretending to be babies.

Piercing, Scarification, and Other Body Modification

The following magazines contain wonderful introductory information and referrals for those who are into having more than their nose pierced. Warning: Piercing, scarification, branding, and other forms of body modification can cause injury or death if done improperly. Proper training and supervision is essential; never attempt these practices without it.

Body Play and Modern Primitives Quarterly
P.O. Box 421668
San Francisco, CA 94142-1668 Sample issue: $12.00

Piercing Fans International Quarterly (PFIQ)
Gauntlet
8720 Santa Monica Blvd.
Los Angeles, CA 90069 Sample issue: $10.00

Prostitute Support Groups

(Mailing addresses only. For sex workers – no would-be customers need write!)

Coyote
2269 Chestnut Street # 452
San Francisco, CA 94123

Coyote – Los Angeles
1626 N. Wilcox Ave. # 580
Hollywood, CA 90028

Prostitutes of New York (PONY)
25 West 45th St., # 1401
New York, New York 10036

Hooking is Real Employment (HIRE)
P.O. Box 89386
Atlanta, GA 39359

Prostitutes Anonymous
11225 Magnolia Blvd. # 181
North Hollywood, CA 91601

For those who want to leave the sex industry or for help afterwards.

Swinging

This form of sexuality used to be called "wife-swapping."

North American Swing Club Association (NASCA)
P.O. Box 7128
Buena Park, CA 90622

Publishes "International Directory of Swing Clubs and Publications."

Sadomasochism

The following organizations are some of the largest. They are open to both men and women. They can provide referrals to those seeking all-male or all-female groups and to those seeking clubs closer to where they live. (Several new clubs form each year.)

Chicagoland Discussion Group
P.O. Box 25009
Chicago, Illinois 60625

Eulenspiegel Society (Believed to be the oldest SM club in the U.S.)
P.O. Box 2783 GCS
New York, New York 10163

Society of Janus
P.O. Box 426794
San Francisco, CA 94142-6794

Threshold
2554 Lincoln Blvd., # 381
Marina Del Rey, CA 90291

Tantra

Tantra, The Magazine
P.O. Box 79
Torreon, New Mexico 87061-9900

Tantra, and its cousins Quodoushka and Healing Tao, are spiritual pathways whose teachings and practices include sexuality. *Tantra, The Magazine* contains excellent listings and descriptions of classes, workshops, and other activities offered around the country.

Transgenderism

For those wishing to change their genders.

FTM (stands for Female-to-Male)
5337 College Ave. # 142
Oakland, CA 94618

San Francisco Gender Information
P.O. Box 423602
San Francisco, CA 94142

Gender Identity Center Newsletter
3715 West 32nd Ave.
Denver, CO 80211

TV/TS Tapestry Journal
Internatonal Foundation for Gender Education (IFGE)
P.O. Box 367
Wayland, MA 01778

Additional Alternative Sexuality Information

San Francisco Sex Information, at (415) 989-7374, offers referrals and a sympathetic ear. They most definitely do not, however, offer phone sex.

Bibliography

"A New View of a Woman's Body" by The Federation of Feminist
Women's Health Centers
published by Feminist Press
8235 Santa Monica Blvd., Suite 201
West Hollywood, CA 90046

"The Complete Guide to Safer Sex"
Institute for Advanced Study of Human Sexuality
1525 Franklin Street
San Francisco, CA 94109

"For Play: 150 Sex Games for Couples"
by Walter Shelburne, Ph.D.
Waterfall Press
5337 College Avenue, #139
Oakland, CA 94618

Condom Educator's Guide, Version Two
by Daniel Bao and Beowulf Thorne
Condom Resource Center
P.O. Box 30564
Oakland, CA 94604
(510) 891-0455

"Sex: A User's Manual"
by The Diagram Group

"Anal Pleasure and Health: A Guide for Men and Women" (Second Edition)
by Jack Morin, Ph.D.
Yes Press
938 Howard Street
San Francisco, CA 94103

"The New Our Bodies, Ourselves: A Book By and For Women"
by The Boston Women's Health Book Collective
A Touchstone Book
 published by Simon and Schuster

"The Good Vibrations Guide to Sex"
by Cathy Winks and Anne Semans
published by Cleis Press

"The Black Book"
edited by Bill Brent
P.O. Box 31155
San Francisco, CA 94131-0155
A comprehensive national guide to sexuality clubs, stores, publications and other resources.

Please Send Me Your Tricks
(but read this carefully first)

Do you do something that consistently drives your lovers wild? Would you like to share your Trick with the rest of us? Send it to me! I plan to publish more "Tricks" books. Maybe you can be a contributor.

Send me your Trick, preferably typed on one side of a standard sheet of paper. Please date the paper and include illustrations as necessary. If I use your Trick, I'll send you a free copy of the book it appears in and, if you wish, put your name on the "thank you" list in that book. Because of "independent discovery" it's impossible for me to credit a particular person with a particular Trick. (I repeatedly encountered independent discovery while researching this book.)

Also, again because of independent discovery, I'll undoubtedly receive letters from different people describing essentially the same Trick, and I can only afford to reward the first person who clearly describes the Trick in question. So, again, please date your letter. (Actually, I'll probably send a book to the first three or so people who send in a given Trick.)

You can increase your chances of inclusion by sending more than one Trick. One per page, please. Please don't send more than ten Tricks a year. I wouldn't have time to properly consider them.

Let me know what type of credit you want on the "thank you" list. You may choose between anonymous, first name only, initials only, your nickname, or your full legal name. If you wish, I can also include your city. If you sign your Trick with your full name, be honest about your identity and include your address and phone number.

Signing another person's name to a letter is a crime, and I will verify all full names before publishing them.

Please send your Trick only by regular first class mail. Spare me from certified letters, registered letters, and so forth. If you don't feel you can trust me, please don't send me your Trick. Also, please don't put a copyright notice on it. A unique usage of words can be copyrighted, but not what such words describe. (This is what allows dozens of reporters to each write a story about the same incident.) Also, I'd almost undoubtedly need to re-write your words while preserving the essence of your Trick.

Please don't send anything "too far out" or dangerous. Letters dealing with children or animals will be immediately turned over to the police.

Please don't send anything regarding political issues, economic concerns, social problems, and so forth. Again, those matters deserve books of their own. (However, if you know of a widely available resource that can help someone with a personal problem closely related to sexuality, I would love to share that information with my readers.)

I was utterly unprepared for the volume of mail that resulted from the publication of my other books. This will add to my load, and I'm already chronically behind in answering that. I therefore can't promise you an individual reply. Including a self-addressed, stamped envelope will help somewhat, but please don't get your hopes up too far. Also, I won't know until just before publication whether or not your Trick was included, so please don't write and ask. You'll know very shortly after I know.

I apologize if the above seems negative and restrictive, but it reflects learning from experience. If you would be happy with a book and being on the "thank you" list, but wouldn't be too disappointed if your Trick didn't make it, then I would genuinely love to hear from you. This world can use a little more pleasure. I hope you help contribute to that.

246